# A DIVERSITY OF
# PUZZLES
Not Only for Experts

*the text of this book is printed
on 100% recycled paper*

# A DIVERSITY OF

# PUZZLES

## Not Only for Experts

## E. R. Emmet

BARNES & NOBLE BOOKS

A DIVISION OF HARPER & ROW, PUBLISHERS

New York, Hagerstown, San Francisco, London

First BARNES & NOBLE BOOKS edition published 1977

LIBRARY OF CONGRESS CATALOG CARD NUMBER: 77–74701
ISBN: 0–06–463463–9

# Contents

(The asterisks indicate how hard the puzzle is, with 5 asterisks for the hardest ones.)

### Part IV   Division: Figures Missing, Figures Wrong

### Part V   The Great Detective

### Part VI   Addition: Letters for Digits

# Preface

This book is in some ways similar to my other books of puzzles, but it also contains some new and different ideas. There are, for example, letters for figures in division and addition problems. This is not in fact a new idea, but some of the puzzles are given a new twist by having *one* of the figures wrong, which tends to produce a harder puzzle than one in which *all* the figures are wrong—after all, in the latter case you know exactly where you are! We also have a few puzzles of various kinds in verse that I hope some people will enjoy; and perhaps best of all, there are the adventures of Professor Knowall and Sergeant Simple.

It is perhaps worth saying a few words about the Professor and the Sergeant. Unlike their great predecessors, who were able to put before the public puzzles of detection in which, generally, all the reader could feel was that the conclusions were reasonably probable, the Professor and the Sergeant have to be quite sure.

Consider, for example, this extract from "The Adventures of Sherlock Holmes," in which Sherlock Holmes is talking to Dr. Watson: "Beyond the obvious fact that he has at some time done manual labor, that he takes snuff, that he is a Frenchman, that he has been in China, and that he has done a considerable amount of writing lately, I can deduce nothing else." These may be very reasonable and helpful conclusions that make it more likely that the villains will be found, but they are not and cannot be certain. The reason is that Sherlock

Holmes and Dr. Watson, though they are fictional characters, are living in an open-system world where the unexpected may happen, where all the data do not have to be revealed. Although it is desirable that the reader be convinced that what happens is likely, he or she does not necessarily have to be told everything. The Professor and the Sergeant, on the other hand, have to stick to stricter rules. The evidence must on the whole be conclusive, and sufficient to produce the answer for which the reader is asked (though in a few cases the reader may be told that the problem cannot be solved completely).

The reader will find old friends (or enemies) on the Island of Imperfection and in Our Factory. But whether we are on the Island, in New York, or wherever the seven workers in Our Factory may be, we have to realize that although sometimes we may not be able to reach the whole truth of the matter, we can be certain as far as we go. It is important to remember that if you are a Wotta-Woppa you must not let the tribe down—you must consistently tell lies every time.

I have been asked by many readers to include a greater number of easier puzzles in my next book, and this I have done. In order to assist readers to find the easier ones (if that is what they want), each puzzle has from one to five stars attached to it. The one-star ones are the easiest and the five-star ones the hardest. But of course I must make the obvious point that to some extent how hard or easy the puzzles are is a matter of opinion, and a sauce that may slip down easily for the goose may be almost indigestible for the gander.

Some of these problems have been adapted from questions in my *Learning to Think*, published by Longmans, and several of them were used as brainteasers in the British *Sunday Times* and subsequently appeared in *The Sunday Times Brain Teasers*, published by Penguin Books; some have appeared in the *New Scientist*. But most of them have not previously appeared in print. I am grateful to the *Sunday Times*, to the *New Scientist*, to Pelican Books, and to Longmans for permission to reprint or to use the ideas again.

Mistakes matter a great deal in a book of this kind, and therefore those who find them and correct the manuscript are especially deserving of an author's gratitude. Many friends have helped me when they were asked—sometimes almost compelled—to do a problem, but among them I would mention particularly, as checkers of almost all the puzzles in the book, Anthony Merriman, David Hall, Hugh Purser, and John Gaskell. I am also most grateful to Letitia Scott for allowing me to reproduce puzzle number 37, which was made up especially for her.

As I have suggested, the checking of a book like this is not easy, nor is the typing of it. Once more, for all the hard and skillful work she has put into this task I am most grateful to Mrs. J. H. Preston.

# PART I

## Various

(1–6)

# 1. The Birthweek (*)

Alf, Bert, Charlie, Douggie, Ernie, and Fred have their birthdays on consecutive days, but not necessarily in that order.

Douggie's birthday is as many days before Alf's as it is after Fred's. Charlie's birthday is as many days before Fred's as Bert's is after Fred's. This year Ernie's birthday is on a Saturday.

On what day of the week do the birthdays of the other 5 men fall this year?


# 2. Today and Today and Today (**)

Alf, Bert, Charlie, Douggie, Ernie, Fred, and George are having an argument about what day of the week it is. They speak as follows:

ALF: The day before yesterday was either Friday or Saturday.

BERT: No, you are quite wrong. Today is Saturday.

CHARLIE: I am never very good at days of the week, but I am sure today is not Saturday, nor is it Sunday or Monday.

DOUGGIE: The day before 2 days after tomorrow is Tuesday.

ERNIE: Tomorrow is one of my workdays, so it cannot be Friday, Saturday, Sunday, or Monday.

FRED: Tomorrow is my birthday, so I know it is Friday.

GEORGE: You are wrong. Today is *my* birthday, and it is 39 days before Christmas, which is on a Friday this year.

Only one of these remarks is true. Which one? Can you say what day of the week it is?

# 3. "I Would If I Could" (***)

"I would if I could, but I'm sorry I can't."
I felt that I had to say this to my Aunt.
She seemed to expect me to lend her some cash.
And, knowing my Aunt, that would surely be rash.
I happen to know what her overdraft is;
My Uncle's is large, hers is much more than his.
Her husband, my Uncle, in fact owed the bank
A number of pounds that was, let's be frank,
Sixty-three more than my overdraft then.
Auntie's and mine are two hundred and ten—
Between them, I mean—and I'd like you to see,
When I say "much," Aunt's is Uncle's times three—
Or as near to three as it can be,
Bearing in mind this vital fact:
The pounds we owe are all exact.
    What are the overdrafts of my Aunt, my Uncle, and myself?

# 4. Rotten Row (***)

It was important for me that I discover the numbers of the houses of 8 acquaintances of mine (whom I shall call A, B, C, D, E, F, G, and H) in Rotten Row. It is an affluent society that they live in, and of course they each have a house. But in spite of higher standards of living and more and better education there are still a lot of people who believe there is a hoodoo on the number 7, and no one can be persuaded to live in it, though it has recently been redecorated.

The Row has houses numbered from 2 to 29 inclusive (number 1 was bombed several wars ago), and I have it on very good authority that one of my 8 acquaintances lives in number 29.

My acquaintances make statements about their house numbers as follows:

A says that his number is twice F's.
B says that his number is 10 more than D's.
C says that his number is 3 more than F's.
D says that his number is 5 more than E's.
E says that his number is $\frac{1}{3}$ of B's.
F says that his number is 6 less than A's.
G says that his number is 6 more than C's.
H says that his number is 9 more than G's.

Unfortunately, one of these statements is not true. Which one? Find the numbers of all the houses.

# 5. The Alternate Lie Drug (***)

Dr. Try and Dr. See have recently come to live in 2 separate houses on Curious Crescent, which has houses numbered from 10 to 90 inclusive. They have been experimenting with a new, very sophisticated drug designed to cause those who take it to make statements that are alternately true and false or false and true. Orders, an intelligent but simple soul who can be relied upon to do what he is told, and who has lived on the Crescent for some time (in a different house of course), has agreed to help them with their experiments. At the time when this story starts, none of them knows the numbers of the houses of either of the other 2.

Dr. Try asks Orders, who has just taken the drug, two questions:

1. Is the number of your house a perfect square?
2. Is the number of your house a multiple of 3?

After a pause for reflection and mathematics, Dr. Try says, "I know the number of Orders's house" and goes on to say what he thinks it is. But he is wrong. (This is not surprising, since although the drug has been working according to plan, Dr. Try was misinformed about the truthfulness of the statement made by Orders immediately preceding the answers to Try's questions.)

Dr. See has heard nothing of what has happened so far, but before he sets about asking Orders questions, there is a general conversation among the 3 of them during which Dr. Try tells the others the number of his own house.

Dr. See's questions to Orders are as follows:

1. Does your number end in 1?
2. Is your number a prime?

After a pause, Dr. See says what he thinks Orders's number is. But he, too, is wrong. And again this is due to the fact that, though the drug has not failed, Dr. See was wrong about which of Orders's answers was right and which one was wrong.

Find the numbers of Dr. Try's, Dr. See's, and Orders's houses. (Note: The difference between Orders's number and that of one of the others is 26.)

# 6. Dothemens Hall (*****)

Miss Machiavel teaches the sixth form for logic at Dothemens Hall, a very modern school for girls. She has always maintained that in order to make friends and influence men a girl must see clearly the vital distinction between what is true and what is false. "If you want warm fingers and a cozy home," she has said, "you must be prepared to play with the fire of deception." Another of her homely adages: "If a lie is worth telling, it is worth telling thoroughly."

After they had heard the results of their advanced-level papers in logic, therefore, Miss Machiavel got 4 of her pupils—Priscilla, Queenie, Rachel, and Susan—to make various remarks, which should all be false, about their grades. (There are 7 possibilities: A candidate may get grade A, B, C, D, or E at the advanced level, or she may get an ordinary-level grade [O] or fail [F]. The possibilities, therefore, in order of merit, are A, B, C, D, E, O, and F.)

The remarks made were as follows:

PRISCILLA: 1. No one had a grade higher than B.
2. Queenie's grade was lower than B.
QUEENIE: 1. My grade was A.
2. Priscilla got one of the 3 highest grades.
RACHEL: 1. My grade was higher than D.
2. Susan's grade was higher than Priscilla's.
SUSAN: 1. My grade was lower than E.
2. Queenie's grade was higher than Rachel's.

Unfortunately, the girls' logic training had not been completely successful and one of these 8 remarks was true, though the other 7 were false. Which one was true? Find each girl's grade. (Note: Their grades were all different.)

# PART II

## Our Factory

(7–15)

# 7. The Factory Accountant (*)

Alf, Bert, Charlie, and Douggie were speculating about which of 4 candidates—Pilfer, Quick, Robbing, and Subtract—will be appointed to keep the factory accounts.

Alf thought that it would certainly not be Quick, but that it might be either Pilfer or Subtract.

Bert was of the opinion that it might be Robbing or Subtract. "The other 2," he said scornfully, "are unintelligent and unqualified."

"As long as it is not Pilfer or Subtract," said Charlie, "I shall be happy."

"Not Quick," said Douggie. "That's all I ask. He cannot add, and he is a crook."

Only one of the 4 had his hope and expectations satisfied.
Who was appointed?

# 8. The Boss's Birthday (**)

I could not help overhearing an argument the other day between my 7 employees—Alf, Bert, Charlie, Douggie, Ernie, Fred, and George—about the month in which my birthday occurs. I must admit that I was rather interested in this, for it seemed to be connected with a suggestion about recognizing it in some way.

The conversation took place on May 1 and went as follows:

ALF: I have heard him say how wonderful it is having a birthday in a month that starts with one of the 2 letters in the middle of the alphabet. He seems to me rather to overestimate the advantages of that. In fact I think he is crazy!

BERT: His birthday is not this month or next, but either the one after that or the one after that.

CHARLIE: I have often heard him say what a disadvantage it has been having a birthday in the winter. He went on to say that he meant the first 2 or the last 3 months of the year.

DOUGGIE: He told me some time ago that his birthday is in a month with only 30 days.

ERNIE: I asked him only the other day, and he said it was in October.

FRED: I know that it is not in the last 3 months or the first 3 months of the year.

GEORGE: You are too late this year; he has had his birthday already.

In fact only one of these statements was true. Which one? Can you say in which month my birthday occurs?

# 9. How to Be Horizontal and First (***)

They simply don't seem to be able to stop (Alf, Bert, Charlie, Douggie, Ernie, and Fred, I mean) in their insatiable desire to do better than their friends. In their latest competition they were having a race backward, horizontally over a 100-yard course. When they had become vertical again they each made one remark as follows:

ALF: I was more than one place behind Fred.
BERT: I was 3 places ahead of Fred.
CHARLIE: Alf beat me.
DOUGGIE: I was 2 places ahead of Alf.
ERNIE: I was not last.
FRED: Ernie was 2 places behind me.

Unfortunately, one of these remarks was not true. It was the one made by the man who won the race; perhaps he was just being modest.

What was the order of the 6 participants in the race?

# 10. Our Factory Has a Holiday Outing (***)

With the increasing standard of living, the members of my factory think more and more of the delights of travel abroad. And once they have tasted these delights, there is no place they would rather go than the Island of Imperfection, where lies can be told proudly and as of right, as they were in the golden age.

There are 3 tribes on this island: the Pukkas, who always tell the truth; the Wotta-Woppas, who never tell the truth; and the Shilli-Shallas, who make statements that are alternately true and false or false and true. This story deals with four members of Our Factory—Alf, Bert, Charlie, and Douggie—whose jobs (not necessarily respectively) were, when they were last working in this country, those of door opener, door shutter, welfare officer, and bottle washer. Each of the 3 tribes has at least one representative in Our Factory, but I am afraid I can give no information about the tribe to which the fourth man belongs.

They make statements as follows:

ALF:  1. The welfare officer is a Wotta-Woppa.
      2. Only one of us is a Pukka.
BERT:  1. Alf is a Pukka.
      2. Charlie is the welfare officer.
CHARLIE: 1. I am a Wotta-Woppa.
      2. Douggie is the door shutter.
DOUGGIE: 1. The door opener is a Shilli-Shalla.
      2. Charlie is not a Wotta-Woppa.

Find the jobs that Alf, Bert, Charlie, and Douggie had when they were last in this country, and the tribes to which they belong on the Island of Imperfection.

# 11. The Richer, the Truer (***)

We have been having some trouble in Our Factory over decimal currency, and it has been agreed that for an interim period of 5 years, until we all get accustomed to the loss of our well-loved shillings, all wages shall be exact multiples of 50p. (And who shall blame us if we secretly think of this as 10 shillings?)

Alf, Bert, and Charlie, whose jobs in the factory (not necessarily respectively) are those of door opener, bottle washer, and sweeper-upper, are having a conversation about their wages, which are none of them less than £14 or greater than £20 a week.

They make remarks as follows:

ALF:      1. My wages are a multiple of 7p.
          2. The sweeper-upper is paid £3 more than the bottle washer.

BERT:     1. The bottle washer is paid less than Charlie.
          2. My wages are an exact number of pounds.

CHARLIE:  1. I am paid £3 less than Alf.
          2. The door opener's wages are £14.50.

These remarks are not, unfortunately, all true. It is interesting to notice that the better paid a man is, the more truthful he is. (Their wages are all different.)

Find the occupation and the wages of each man. (Note: The fact that Alf makes a remark about the bottle washer does not imply that he is not the bottle washer.)

# 12.  Sharing Power in Our Factory (***)

I do not work, I merely sit and think.
Think of the joys of yesteryear, and how
My workers all obeyed me at a wink.
Long, long ago! They would not do so now.
   For now they share the power, decisions make,
   And see to it that none of them is bored.
   There's a recession, we must not produce
   Too much. Sell three a week, the rest is stored.
And so, a subtle move, four men will be
Enough, it's thought, for the eight jobs required;
And they can then share power, you will agree,
And boredom too—unless, of course, they're fired!
   Consider now, especially, he who makes tea for eight.
   "But what else do you do?" I asked. "I sit and meditate
   About the welfare of the staff. They call me the tea boy,
   But welfare too, I always say, for that's my other ploy."
   (But tea for only *four* you think, but surely you can see
   That if a man is doing two jobs he needs two cups of tea.)
Who is the worker? The opener of the door?
No! Nor is the bottle washer he who shuts them.
And in Our Factory you can be quite sure
That what the worker does is much "ad rem."
Or, rather, what he does not do. Remember, please,
He would not wash a bottle, if asked on bended knees.
   Charlie does not shut a door, no bottles pass Doug's hand.
   Alf does the task of sweeping up. Bert takes a powerful stand:
   No worker he, he has been told just what a worker's for.
   And of Douggie's two jobs neither is connected with a door.
No opening of doors is done by Bert.
The problem now is yours. Be swift, alert.
   What are the two jobs of Alf, Bert, Charlie, and Douggie?
(The jobs are those of sweeper-upper, door opener, door shutter,
doorknob polisher, welfare officer, bottle washer, tea boy, and
worker.)

# 13. Higher Thinking in Our Factory (****)

|  | Number of question | | | | | | Total for each person |
|---|---|---|---|---|---|---|---|
|  | 1 | 2 | 3 | 4 | 5 | 6 |  |
| Alf | 20 | $3.15 | 30 | 8 | $125 | 15% | 15 |
| Bert | 26 | $10.10 | 38 | 7 | $110 | 20% |  |
| Charlie | 18 | $2.40 | 35 | 12 | $100 | 15% | 25 |
| Douggie | 20 | $1.10 | 43 | 7 | $108 | 23% | 5 |
| Ernie | 26 | $2.40 | 38 | 12 | $120 | 50% | 35 |
| Total for each question |  | 10 |  | 20 |  | 35 |  |

The preceding table shows the answers given by the members of Our Factory—Alf, Bert, Charlie, Douggie, and Ernie—in a mathematics examination. There are also some particulars about the total number of marks gained by each person and for each question.

If the answer was right, 10 marks were given. If the answer was wrong, 0 or 5 marks were given according to the method used. (If 2 people get the same wrong answer, it is quite possible for one of them to get 5 and the other 0.)

At least one person got each question right.

What are the right answers to the 6 questions?

# 14. The End of an Era (****)

There comes a time in every man's life when, however important his job may be, he has to think of retirement. It is with this thought in mind that I have recently been considering the question of my successor. I have, after all, seen what some friends have kindly described as the fantastic growth of the factory from a payroll of 5 to one of 7.

In order to choose my new managing director I decided to use a new and little-known technique (of which I am afraid the details must still be kept secret) for assessing what used to be called "officerlike qualities."

After the test was over, my 7 employees—Alf, Bert, Charlie, Douggie, Ernie, Fred, and George—did not know either their own place or anyone else's. This did not, however, prevent them from speculating about them. (There were no ties in the test.)

They spoke as follows:

ALF:     I feel pretty sure that I beat Charlie.

BERT:    I would be very surprised if I did not beat Ernie.

CHARLIE: 1. I don't much like making guesses about how other people did, but I would certainly have expected Alf to be higher than George.
2. My guess is that Fred was 2 places above me.

DOUGGIE: 1. Bert was below George, in my opinion.
2. It may be conceited of me, but I feel sure that I was above Charlie.

ERNIE:   I would expect Bert to have been 3 places above Douggie.

FRED:    I feel sure that I was higher than Alf.

GEORGE:  I think that Douggie was probably higher than Alf.

These were, I am sure, all honest men doing their best, and it is interesting that all but one of their speculations were correct.

Find the order of merit in the test.

# 15. When Rules Were Rules and Pounds Were Pounds (*****)

No organization can be efficient without clear-cut rules setting out exactly the rewards and the responsibilities of those who have the honor to be members of the team. The other day I came across a copy of the rules that I, as the managing director of Our Factory, had put on the Society's notice board for all to see and understand. But this was many years ago, when the pound was worth something, and when rules were obeyed.

There were 5 employees in the factory then, and their names were Alf, Bert, Charlie, Douggie, and Ernie. Their jobs (not necessarily respectively) were those of door opener, door shutter, doorknob polisher, bottle washer, and welfare officer.

The notice that I put up read as follows:

*Rules*

1. Charlie is to get 10 percent more than the worst paid of you all.
2. Alf is to be paid more than Douggie.
3. The bottle washer is to get 5 percent more than 10 percent less than Bert.
4. Douggie is to get either £1 more or £1 less than Ernie.
5. The door opener's wages are to be an odd multiple of 10p.
6. Ernie is to get 20 percent more than £1 less than the doorknob polisher.
7. The door shutter is to be the best paid of you all.
8. Your wages are all to be different, and each is to be a multiple of 10p.
9. No one is to get more than £20 or less than £10 per week.

What are their weekly wages?

# PART III

---

# Soccer

(16–23)

---

# 16.  Three Teams: All Figures Correct (*)

Three soccer teams—A, B, and C—play against each other.
The following table gives some information about the results:

|   | Played | Won | Lost | Drawn | Goals for | Goals against |
|---|--------|-----|------|-------|-----------|---------------|
| A | 2      |     | 2    |       | 2         |               |
| B | 2      |     |      |       | 3         |               |
| C | 2      |     |      | 1     | 2         | 0             |

Find the score in each match.

# 17.  Four Teams: All Figures Correct (**)

In a competition among 4 soccer teams—A, B, C, and D—
each team is to play each of the others once.

After some of the matches have been played, a table giving
a certain amount of information about the number of matches
played, won, lost, and drawn and the goals for and against
each team reads as follows:

|   | Played | Won | Lost | Drawn | Goals for | Goals against |
|---|--------|-----|------|-------|-----------|---------------|
| A | 3      |     |      |       | 2         |               |
| B | 2      |     |      | 1     | 0         | 3             |
| C |        | 3   |      |       | 7         |               |
| D |        |     |      | 1     | 3         | 5             |

Find the score in each match played.

# 18.  Uncle Bungle Again (**)

In Uncle Bungle's latest "table" of soccer matches played
the only decipherable figures were in the "Goals for" and
"Goals against" columns.
These read as follows:

| Goals for | Goals against |
|:---------:|:-------------:|
| 2 | 4 |
|   | 2 |
| 5 | 4 |

We shall assume that there were 3 teams, each of which was
to play against each other team once, and that the preceding
table represents the situation after some—or perhaps all—of
the matches had been played. (I discovered from another
source that at least one of the matches was drawn.)

Calling the teams A, B, and C, in that order, find the score in
each match.

# 19.  The Lie Drug (**)

The doctor in our little village has for a long time been experimenting with lie drugs, and one afternoon he was trying out
his latest concoction on the secretary of one of the 3 local
soccer teams (A, B, and C).

The secretary had just been given a powerful dose and
seemed to be in a coma as he sat trying, at the doctor's request,
to fill in the numbers of matches played, won, lost, and so on.
(Each of the 3 teams is to play each other team once.)

Suddenly the doctor snatched the piece of paper from the
secretary with a cry of delight. "Success!" he said. "Every
single figure here is incorrect!"

I looked at the document, which read as follows:

|   | Played | Won | Lost | Drawn | Goals for | Goals against | Points |
|---|--------|-----|------|-------|-----------|---------------|--------|
| A |        | 0   |      |       |           |               | 2      |
| B | 1      |     |      | 0     | 1         |               |        |
| C |        | 1   |      | 1     | 0         | 1             | 0      |

(2 points for a win; 1 for a draw)

I found it interesting that—perhaps because of a sub-
conscious desire for truth in spite of the drug—though all
the figures given were incorrect, it was nonetheless possible
to discover details of all the matches played.

Find who played whom and the score in each match. (Not
more than 3 goals were scored in any match.)

# 20. A Diversity of Scores (***)

Four soccer teams—A, B, C, and D—were all to play each other once. After some—or perhaps all—the matches had been played, I discovered that a total of 18 goals had been scored and that B had scored 2 more than each of the other 3 teams. B also had 3 times as many goals scored against it as D had, and A had the same number of goals against it as for it. C had fewer goals scored against it than any of the other teams.

It was interesting to notice that in every match both sides scored at least one goal, and that in no matches were the scores exactly the same. One match was drawn.

Find the scores in all the matches that were played.

# 21. Some Sticky Impedimenta (***)

Uncle Bungle's carelessness and untidiness get more exasperating every day. He has always been very interested in soccer, and I thought I could rely on him to let me know the situation in a set of matches in which 5 local teams—A, B, C, D, and E—were each to play each of the others once.

All he was prepared to do, however, was to give me a messy piece of paper on which red ink had been fighting a losing battle against the assorted and mainly sticky impedimenta that my uncle kept in his pocket. I copied out what I could decipher, as follows:

|   | Played | Won | Lost | Drawn | Goals for | Goals against | Points |
|---|--------|-----|------|-------|-----------|---------------|--------|
| A | 3 |   |   |   | 2 | 4 | 3 |
| B | 3 |   |   |   |   | 0 |   |
| C |   |   |   | 0 | 1 | 1 |   |
| D | 4 |   |   | 0 |   | 0 |   |
| E |   |   | 2 |   | 1 |   | 1 |

I had just finished the copying when I heard the voice of my uncle in my ear. "You really ought to be more careful," he said. "You've got one of those figures wrong."

Which is the incorrect figure, and what should it be? What was the score in each match?

# 22.  A Subdued Uncle (***)

Uncle Bungle has become so careless in making up his soccer puzzles that the authorities have decided that no further mistakes will be tolerated. It was, therefore, a subdued, chastened, and very much more careful uncle who after many hours of thought produced the following:

| | Played | Won | Lost | Drawn | Goals for | Goals against | Points |
|---|---|---|---|---|---|---|---|
| A | | 2 | | 1 | 6 | 5 | |
| B | | | 2 | | | 2 | 0 |
| C | | | | | | 8 | |
| D | 4 | | | 2 | 5 | 5 | |
| E | | | 0 | | 0 | | 2 |

(2 points for a win; 1 for a draw. Each team is eventually to play each other team once.)

Readers may be surprised to know that for once uncle's efforts had been completely successful. There were no mistakes. Find the scores in all the matches.

# 23. The False Drug Fails (*****)

Dr. W.O.T.A.-Woppa, a Chinese expert in false drugs, has been making experiments to test the effectiveness of his latest discovery, designed, of course, to ensure that no light of truth shall shine through the utterances of those who take it.

The secretaries of 4 local soccer teams, which were having a competition in which the teams were each to play each other team once, were all given a pill just before each of them made a statement about the number of matches played, won, lost, and drawn; the goals scored for and against; and the points obtained by his team (2 points for a win; 1 for a draw).

These statements, combined, were as follows:

|   | Played | Won | Lost | Drawn | Goals for | Goals against | Points |
|---|--------|-----|------|-------|-----------|---------------|--------|
| A | 3 | 1 | 1 | 0 | 0 | 1 | 1 |
| B | 3 | 0 | 0 | 0 | 0 | 2 | 2 |
| C | 2 | 0 | 1 | 0 | 3 | 2 | 5 |
| D | 2 | 0 | 0 | 0 | 4 | 2 | 3 |

Dr. Woppa was disappointed to discover that the drug had not been completely successful. In fact two of the figures in the table were true.

Find who played whom and the score in each match. (The teams are not necessarily listed in order of merit; indeed, D got more points than B. Not more than 3 goals were scored in any match.)

# PART IV

---

# Division:
# Figures Missing,
# Figures Wrong

## (24–27)

---

## 24. Six Digits Divided by Two Digits (**)

A division sum. Find the missing digits.

```
              2 - - - · -
        ┌─────────────────
  - - ) - - 0 - - 1
        - -
        ─────
        - - -
        - - -
        ─────
          - - 7
          - - -
          ─────
            - - -
            - - -
            ═════
```

## 25. Seven Digits Divided by Two Digits (***)

A division sum. Find the missing digits. (In the complete answer there are *two* 5's.)

## 26. Six Digits Divided by Two Digits: Figures Given All Wrong (***)

In the following division sum the figures given are all wrong and the figures in the quotient are all different. Find all the figures of the correct sum.

```
                _ _ _ _
      2 2 ) _ 0 _ _ _ _
              8 9
            ‾‾‾‾‾
              _ _ _
              1 1 9
                _ _
                6 0
              ‾‾‾‾
                  _ _
                  _ _
                  ═══
```

## 27. Five Digits Divided by Two Digits: Figures Given All Wrong (*****)

In the following division sum the figures given are all wrong. Find the correct figures.

```
                1 7 8 6
      3 4 ) 9 _ _ _ _
            6 0
          ‾‾‾
            1 _ _
            2 8 6
          ‾‾‾‾‾
              3 _ _
              1 4 3
            ‾‾‾‾‾
                3 1 _
                2 _ _
              ‾‾‾‾‾
                ═══
```

# PART V

## The Great Detective

(28–38)

# 28. The Woogle on the Wardrobe (*)

I thought Professor Knowall looked at me rather strangely as I came into the office one day, and I was a bit worried, for he usually takes me and my appearance for granted.

"You don't look, my dear Sergeant Simple," he said, "as though you had a very good night's sleep."

I was amazed by his perception. In a flash he had seen not only that I was not feeling quite myself, but also why. The least I could do, I felt, was to tell him all—to hold nothing back, but to give him more information about the sleepless nights that I had been having.

The situation had not been helped by the fact that the last few nights had been rather windy. I had heard, as I lay in bed, an intermittent high-pitched squeak and a regular dull thud.

I got out of bed, clasped with one hand the woogle that hangs outside my wardrobe and with the other the chumph that is loose on the top of my chest of drawers, and steadied with my foot the pollux, which is normally free to move around the floor on casters. The thud stopped, but the squeak continued.

I kept hold of the chumph, seized with my other hand the Venetian blind, and transferred my foot to the rocking chair. The squeak stopped and there was still no thud.

I then kept hold of the Venetian blind, seized the woogle once more, and took my foot off the rocking chair. The thud started up again, but there was still no squeak.

But what could I do? I knew that the Professor would approve of my making these experiments, but no man can control woogles, chumphs, polluxes, Venetian blinds, and rocking chairs all at once, and I had been unable to come to any conclusions as to what caused the noise.

The Professor, with the information that I had given him, solved the problem in less time than it takes to steady a pollux.

What can you say about the causes of the two noises?

# 29. The Quill Quirks (*)

Professor Knowall, as was his habit, took a long, close look at the latest superb example of modern technology, which sat, as it seemed, uneasily and unhappily on the carpet in front of us.

"We must look back," he said. "Today follows yesterday as the dog follows the cat."

As always, the Professor went straight to the heart of the matter, but I could not refrain from adding a little of my own homespun philosophy.

"What is to be," I said, "will surely be."

"Nonsense, my good Sergeant Simple," said the Professor. "If that were true, we should both be out of a job. But we must stick to our muttons."

I did not see what muttons had to do with the matter, but as always I was prepared to follow my master wherever he led me.

And then I had the great privilege of hearing something of his train of thought.

"What happens, Simple," he said, "when I take off the little cap on the top and press the big button with 'Beware' written on it?" (The Professor can hardly be expected to know much about the names of complicated modern machines.)

There was nothing wrong with my powers of observation, so, fortunately, I was able to answer this question.

"The quill," I said, "will quirk; also the rudder will rumble."

"And what will happen, my dear Simple," said the Professor, "if I take off the little cap on the top, cut open the card saying 'Do not touch,' and dingle the drum marked 'Danger. Do not Dingle'?"

"In that case," I was able to reply, "the rudder will rumble and the springs will squeak."

"One more question," said the Professor. "What will happen now if I press the big button with 'Beware' written on it and dingle the drum marked 'Danger. Do not Dingle'?"

"In that case," I said, "the quill will quirk."

What happened after this may seem to some of my readers almost incredible, but in a very few moments the Professor had solved the problem.

On the assumption that the 3 faults of the machine are caused by single events and not 2 or more in conjunction, what is the cause of each of the machine's faults?

# 30. Some Private Tattering (**)

I have been a keen soccer fan for many years, and I follow with great interest the performance of local and not-so-local teams.

I was rather ashamed, however, when Professor Knowall picked up a tattered piece of paper (which I must have dropped) that had once contained some particulars of 3 soccer teams competing against one another. I was ashamed because, as the Professor had so often said, "tattered bits of paper indicate a tattered mind."

I also felt that if I was to show myself worthy of being the great man's friend and associate my interests ought to be centered on higher things.

But the Professor was clearly interested. After looking at it for only a few minutes he said, "From what I can read of this you have, as usual, made a careless or illegible mistake."

The figures, as the Professor saw them, were as follows:

|   | Played | Won | Lost | Drawn | Goals for | Goals against |
|---|--------|-----|------|-------|-----------|---------------|
| A |        |     |      | 1     |           | 0             |
| B |        |     |      | 2     | 2         | 3             |
| C |        | 1   | 1    |       |           | 6             |

On the assumption that there was just one mistake, what was it? What was the score in all the matches that had been played?

# 31. "Such Stuff as Dreams Are Made Of" (***)

Professor Knowall has recently become very interested in dreams. I think perhaps that this is due to his advancing years, but of course I would not say this to him.

It so happens that a friend of mine, who is the managing director of a factory, has been doing some research on this matter. He has been studying the extent to which dreams can be used to foretell the future and perhaps also to explain the past.

My friend has not found it difficult to persuade some of his employees—whose names are Alf, Bert, Charlie, Douggie, and Ernie—to help him in his inquiries (an ominous phrase for the Professor and me, but it produced no reaction from the simple souls with whom we are dealing). They were prepared to help, I think, because they and their managing director like to be in the forefront of any new idea and also perhaps because their beds seem to them an excellent place for research.

Their first session took place just over a year ago. In it they made predictions about what their jobs would be a year later. Their predictions were as follows:

1. Alf predicted that Ernie would not be the door opener.
2. Bert predicted that Douggie would not be the bottle washer.
3. Charlie predicted that Alf would not be the welfare officer.
4. Douggie predicted that Ernie would be the bottle washer.
5. Ernie predicted that Bert's prediction would prove to be true.

It is interesting to note that the 5 jobs they had at the time were those of bottle washer, welfare officer, door shutter, door opener, and worker (but not necessarily in that order).

When I told the Professor about this experiment he was most interested. "But how many of the predictions, my dear Sergeant Simple, were correct?" he asked, "and most important of all, by whom were the correct predictions made?"

I was able to tell him that only 2 of the predictions were correct, and I think he found this rather disappointing. But he seemed to think that it proved something when I went on to tell him that the 2 correct predictions were made by the men who became the welfare officer and the worker.

He was also, very naturally, interested to find out just what jobs Alf, Bert, Charlie, Douggie, and Ernie hold now, and he deduced this in what seemed to me an incredibly short time. It was one of those problems that are, I am afraid, too much for me, but I am sure my readers will be able to solve it quite easily.

Can you?

# 32.  Wage Negotiation on the Island of Imperfection (***)

It was a great relief to Professor Knowall and to me when, as a change from solving murder mysteries, the authorities on the Island asked us to take on a little matter of wage negotiation. Perhaps I should say that it looked like being a great relief, but by the time we had finished we were almost crying aloud for a few nice, simple corpses. But the story I have to tell here does not go as far as that; it is merely concerned with the preliminary to the preliminaries, the finding out of a few facts that might make possible a discussion as to whether a discussion was possible.

There are 3 tribes on the Island: the Pukkas, who always tell the truth; the Wotta-Woppas, who never tell the truth; and the Shilli-Shallas, who make statements that are alternately true and false or false and true.

The 3 workers whose wages we are to examine are X, Y, and Z, one for each tribe. They are represented in the negotiations by A, B, and C, again one from each tribe. X, Y, and Z have set out their case to A, B, and C, using the now well-tried tribal technique of making 3 remarks each in accordance with their tribal characteristics. It so happens that all the remarks made by A, B, and C had a truth value opposite to that of the corresponding remark made by those whom they represent (e.g., if Y's third remark is true and if B represents Y, then B's third remark is false.)

When the Professor read what I had written so far, he characteristically said, "Why must you always complicate rather than simplify, my dear Sergeant Simple? What you have put in parentheses is much clearer than all that nonsense about truth values. In fact I must confess that I had some difficulty understanding it myself."

They are optimistic people on the Island, as is shown by the fact that they call their currency *hopes*. It is interesting to notice, however, that there is one thing on which all the parties to the discussions are agreed, and this is that they have always been paid in the past, are paid now, and will always be paid in the future a wage that shall be an exact number of hopes. The wages of X, Y, and Z are all between 25 and 85 hopes, inclusive.

A, B, and C make statements as follows:

A 1. The wages of the man whom B represents are 7 less than those of the man whom C represents.
  2. X's first remark is false.
  3. The wages of the man I represent are one-half of one of the others' wages.

B 1. The wages of the man I represent are more than H44.
  2. Z says that his wages are a multiple of 11.
  3. C represents a Wotta-Woppa.

C 1. Y is a Pukka.
  2. Z is a Pukka.
  3. A is a Shilli-Shalla.

I had hoped that I would be able to solve this problem by myself, but I'm afraid that I had to call in the Professor.

To what tribes do A, B, and C and X, Y, and Z belong, and what are X, Y, and Z's wages?

# 33. "Who Did It?" on the Island of Imperfection (***)

Professor Knowall and I had been making a tour of the little-known oceans of the world, and we decided to spend some time on the fabulous Island of Imperfection.

There are 3 tribes on this island: the Pukkas, who always tell the truth; the Wotta-Woppas, who never tell the truth; and the Shilli-Shallas, who make statements that are alternately true and false or false and true.

It did not take us long to discover that even here crime had reared its ugly head. Under conditions that made it plain that a little bit of thieving was involved, the Professor lost his watch. The incident and its aftermath were covered in confusion, but one thing that was quite clear was that the thief must have been one of 6 men whom I shall call A, B, C, D, E, and F (A and D belong to one tribe, B and E to another, and C and F to the third).

"Let us see," I said (rather ingeniously, I thought), "which of them turns up in time if we ask them all to have a drink with us at the local hostelry."

"Not a very sensible suggestion, my dear Sergeant Simple," replied the Professor. "We cannot tell what time it is without a watch."

The Professor did not seem to have gotten my point. I wondered whether he was suffering from a touch of the sun, which was certainly perfect on the Island if nothing else was. But I need have had no fears. I don't know how the Professor organized it, but before we knew where we were, A, B, and C were in front of us making statements (in accordance, of course, with their tribal characteristics). It is important to know that all 6 suspects are between the ages of 20 and 80 inclusive, and that there are at least 3 years between the birthdays of any 2 of them. The relevance of this, as will be seen in the remarks that follow, is that age or lack of it is something that looms very large in the Islanders' thoughts.

The 3 suspects spoke as follows:

A 1. B is older than F.
   2. D is younger than E.
   3. When asked whether B stole the watch, E said yes.
B 1. C is older than D.
   2. The youngest of the six of us is the criminal.
   3. A is 3 times as old as F.
C 1. B stole the watch.
   2. The oldest of the 6 of us is the criminal.
   3. A is a Pukka.

The Professor closed his eyes, and one could almost see his powerful mind working.

"Yes," he said, after what seemed only a few moments. "There is no doubt who the villain is."

Who was the villain? What can you say about the men's ages?

# 34.  A Cold Professor (***)

Professor Knowall and I are not as young as we once were, and we do not like the cold. When our central heating system ceased to operate recently, it therefore seemed very important that we should both give our, if I may say so, powerful minds to discovering what was wrong with it and putting it right. What was wrong with it was, of course, that it did not heat, but I could see that it was important to dig deeper into the matter—and the machine—than that.

I say it did not heat, but that is really an oversimplification. For it did other things instead. But as the Professor, who is of course an expert in this matter, said, "If we can put right, my dear Sergeant Simple, the things that it ought not to be doing, then it will follow as the night the day that it will do the things that it ought to be doing."

Heartened by this assurance (though not feeling entirely happy about the reasoning behind it), I set out the situation as I saw it.

When I turned the central heating $\frac{3}{4}$ on and pressed the button that said "Emergency. Press if all else fails," cold water started to drip from the pipes and there was a high-pitched scream.

When I turned the central heating $\frac{1}{2}$ on and pressed the button that said "For increased oil fluidity," cold water dripped from the pipes and they turned blue.

When I turned the central heating $\frac{3}{4}$ on and pressed the button saying "For increased oil fluidity," the pipes turned blue.

I may not know much about central heating systems, but I know enough about life as a whole and about the connection between cause and effect to realize that what must be done first is to trace the causal links.

What can you say about the causes of the system's 3 defects?

# 35. Murder in the Menonly Mansion (****)

It so happens that the crimes and mysteries that I have recently been recording have been minor ones. Up to now murder had not reared its ugly head. But now it has. And the crime of jealousy or passion that I am about to record for posterity was a particularly unpleasant one, involving as it did some sort of disagreement within a family that had always been regarded as the happy family to end all happy families (and, the events of that terrible day may have done just that).

But let us get to the facts. In the Menonly Mansion 11 male members of the Menonly family had been living. There were 4 brothers and their sons, if any, and their grandsons, if any. The 4 brothers and all their sons and grandsons were all alive on the afternoon with which this story deals.

The names of the 11 were, in alphabetical order, Arthur, Brian, Colin, Duncan, Edgar, Ferdinand, George, Henry, Ivor, Julian, and Kenneth.

The body of Colin was discovered in the attic, where he was in the habit of retiring for the deep philosophical thoughts that made him so different from the other 10. But the mangled state of his corpse made it unlikely that his death was just the result of a philosophical disagreement.

When Professor Knowall and I were called in, it seemed to us important that we should first try to discover rather more about the family tree. I myself held the view that no brothers or fathers or grandfathers or sons or uncles or nephews could have committed such a horrible crime, and that we must look, if we could, for cousins.

But the Professor did not agree with me. "The sort of passion that leads to murder, my dear Sergeant Simple," he said, "is not interested in family or any other trees."

However, this was obviously a possible line of inquiry, and we did what we could to discover more about how the members of the family were related to each other.

We did not, unfortunately, know the names of the 4 original brothers, but we were able to discover the following facts:

1. Arthur, Brian, Colin, Edgar, George, and Henry have sons among the 11.
2. Duncan is George's only grandson.
3. Edgar and George are 2 of Henry's uncles.
4. Colin's only son is Ivor.
5. Julian, who has no brothers, is a nephew of Brian and Kenneth.
6. Brian has 3 brothers.

But we desperately needed more information, and I can seldom remember the normally confident and optimistic Professor being so low in spirits.

"Just for once, Simple," he said, "we need a bit of luck."

And then we got it. In a secret pocket of Colin's gown (which he always wore when he was philosophizing) we found this tattered note:

If I should die there's murder in the Mansion.
"Cherchez la femme"; cherchez too my cousin's only son.

"That's the breakthrough we want, Simple," said the Professor. "I might have known there would be one somewhere."

I suppose he meant a "femme," but I thought he might have said something about the fact that just for once I had made a prediction that was correct.

How, exactly, are the 11 Menonlys related to each other? Who killed Colin?

# 36. Nearly Right (****)

"Detection is what I am interested in, my dear Sergeant Simple," Professor Knowall has often said to me. "And," he is in the habit of going on (for repetition is, I must admit, one of the Professor's very few faults), "I am ready to detect assorted crimes or foolish mistakes made by almost anybody."

Well, I suppose it is reasonable to say that I am almost anybody, and the Professor had certainly discovered something wrong on one of my inky pieces of paper, which contained some details about the soccer matches that were currently being played by 5 local soccer teams.

The figures that could be read were the following:

|   | Played | Won | Lost | Drawn | Goals for | Goals against | Points |
|---|--------|-----|------|-------|-----------|---------------|--------|
| A | 3      |     | 1    | 2     |           |               | 2      |
| B | 4      | 3   |      | 1     | 5         |               | 7      |
| C |        | 1   | 1    |       |           | 2             |        |
| D | 2      |     | 2    |       | 3         | 5             | 0      |
| E | 3      |     | 2    | 0     | 3         | 2             | 2      |

(2 points for a win; 1 point for a draw)

Each team was eventually to play each other team once.

Actually, the Professor was making rather a fuss about the matter, for only one of the figures was wrong.

Which figure is wrong? Find the scores in all the matches that had been played.

# 37. Tish and the Rajah's Rubies (****)

It was a frightened, breathless, but very charming young lady who knocked on my office door late one September night.

"They have gone," she said. "The Rajah's rubies are no longer in their ancestral home!"

However charming young ladies may be, it is important in my opinion to give them all the correct "Sergeant" treatment. I therefore suggested that she sit in the confessional chair and tell me all.

For our present purposes her long story must be cut rather short. There seemed little doubt that the rubies to which she referred had indeed disappeared. I did not think it possible that a lady with so obvious a ruby fixation could have made a mistake about this. But fortunately she had discovered near the scene of the crime a tattered piece of paper on which there were a large number of digits and some rather curiously arranged letters, some of which were illegible.

It did not take me long to decide that it was the digits, not the letters, that were likely to help us, and I immediately suggested to the young lady (I had discovered by this time that her name was Letitia and her friends called her Tish) that I should ring up Professor Knowall, who included among his many accomplishments an almost inconceivable skill at decoding.

Before I could say "Tish" 2 or 3 times the Professor was with us, and he seemed to know by instinct that what mattered was not the tearful eye of Letitia or her rather confused evidence but the tattered piece of paper.

I explained that in my judgment the letters were meaningless and we ought to concentrate on the digits.

"That, my dear Sergeant Simple," said the Professor, "is just where you are wrong. Letters are very rarely meaningless. Always look at the whole forest, not just a tree or two. The first thing we must do is to set out all the evidence neatly and tidily."

This he then proceeded to do, and it looked like this:

4936270681427669705719691270187069477266

```
                o  -  s  u
          _____
   n u ) -  d  e  e  f  -
          n  u
          _____
          u  r  -
          d  t  e
          _____
             s  h  -
             u  t  -
             _____
                d  f  d
                d  t  -
                _____
                      t
                      =
```

What was the message on the tattered piece of paper?

# 38. Not After Jay (*****)

Dr. Chris Cross had been a friend of mine for many years, and I was shocked and surprised when the telephone rang one evening and his housekeeper informed me that he had died suddenly. The housekeeper had gotten in touch with me not only because she knew that I was an old friend but also because Cross's departure hardly seemed to be a result of natural causes. For one thing, he was found lying prostrate on the floor of the lounge, whereas he usually preferred to be prostrate on the floor of the study. Another unusual thing the house-keeper found that made her rather suspicious was a pool of blood under the corpse, and there was also a very large bump on the back of Cross's head.

I wasted no time in calling up Professor Knowall and arranging to meet him at Cross's house. My mind moved pretty quickly in such a situation, and the more I thought about it the more it seemed that we had in front of us the opportunity—and also, of course, the responsibility—of investigating what could only be described as a dastardly crime.

When the Professor and I viewed Cross's corpse we found (not surprising to someone who knew him as I did) a cross-number puzzle in his hand. He was a great one for making up puzzles of this kind, and it did not seem to me that this one had any particular significance. The Professor, however, seemed to think otherwise.

"Listen to this, my dear Sergeant Simple," he said. "The title is 'Not After Jay'."

Naturally I wanted to know who Jay was, but all that the Professor would say was that there were Jays and Jays—a pretty cryptic and, it seemed to me, not very sensible remark.

I took it upon myself to make a few inquiries about the people Cross had been seeing lately. The housekeeper knew his acquaintances or his callers only by their Christian names. She mentioned Douggie, George, Alf, Hubert, Abe, John,

Ian, Eddie, and Peter as being among those who had called on Cross recently, and it seemed to me to be possible, but by no means certain, that the man we must look for was one of them. But more clues were desperately needed.

While I had been looking closely for fingerprints and using my increasingly powerful mind on the problem that we had in front of us, I was exceedingly disappointed to see that the Professor seemed to have nothing better to do than waste his time on that rather silly cross-number puzzle.

And then, suddenly, he sprang to his feet.

"Yes," he said. "Not after Jay indeed!" This seemed to me to be a stupid and pointless remark, and I wondered whether his mind was becoming a little unhinged by the strain of solving the cross-number puzzle.

But he went on to say, "The mystery has now been solved, my dear Sergeant Simple. And I think we should immediately make an arrest."

The cross-number puzzle was as follows:

| 1 | 2 | 3 | 4 | 5 |
|---|---|---|---|---|
| 6 |   |   |   |   |
|   | 7 |   |   | 8 |
|   | 9 |   |   |   |
| 10 |  |   |   |   |

*Across*

1. The sum of the digits is 32.
6. The average size of the digits in this number is 4.
7. The digits are all different, and all less than 5.
9. To get the first 2 digits of this even number, subtract 1 from the number formed by the last 2 digits and multiply by 2.

54

10. Odd. One digit appears 3 times in this number, and another one, larger but less than 6, appears twice.

*Down*
1. The first 3 figures of 3 down multiplied by the second digit of 2 down.
2. A multiple of 3.
3. Add 4 to the last digit and this number would be the same when reversed. The second digit subtracted from the first digit is equal to the third digit subtracted from the second.
4. Even. But all the other digits are odd, and one of them (but not the smallest one) appears twice.
5. The same as the first 2 digits of 3 down. A multiple of 3 and of 7.
7. The same when reversed.
8. The result of multiplying 2 numbers that differ by 2. One is a prime number and the other has 2 factors.

Who does the Professor think should be arrested, and why?

# PART VI

## Addition:
## Letters for Digits

(39–42)

## 39. Addition: Letters for Digits (Two Numbers) (*)

Following is an addition sum with letters substituted for digits. The same letter stands for the same digit whenever it appears, and different letters stand for different digits. Write the sum out with numbers substituted for letters.

```
  A B L B
  B G L B
---------
  L Z A A
=========
```

## 40. Addition: Letters for Digits (Three Numbers) (**)

Following is an addition sum with letters substituted for digits. The same letter stands for the same digit wherever it appears, and different letters stand for different digits. Write the sum out with numbers substituted for letters.

```
  D H E S
  J H H S
  R H D S
---------
  H H J H
=========
```

# 41. "I Do Not Wish to Be, I'd Like to Add" (**)

I do not wish to be,
   I'd like to add.
Being is all a matter of degree,
   I know this well,
But my decision just to be no more
   Is not a fad.
It comes from an experience of life second to none.
It means that I have said, no love, no laughter,
Mechanization's what I want and see what follows after.
   It is not mad
   To want to add,
   Nor is it bad.
It leads to certainty, and that is what I have a passion for,
"Why yes, perhaps it is, perhaps it's not," no more, no more.
For now the great adventure, the hour when I cease to exist
And just become a computer, no life but also no risk.
   Perhaps you think my no-life has no future.
   To show you're wrong I offer you a test.
   Letters for digits, add something to "COMPUTER"
   And you will find certainty, peace, and rest.

$$
\begin{array}{cccccccc}
 & C & O & M & P & U & T & E & R \\
 & T & A & P & R & U & R & C & R \\
\hline
 & C & O & A & X & O & X & P & R & O \\
\end{array}
$$

Write the sum out with numbers substituted for letters.

# 42. Addition: Letters for Digits (Four Numbers: One Letter Wrong) (***)

In Uncle Bungle's latest addition sum with letters substituted for digits, 4 numbers, each containing 4 digits, have been added together. That being the case, and considering the number of mistakes he might have made, it must, I think, be regarded as surprising that only one letter is wrong. The same letter should stand for the same digit wherever it appears, and different letters should stand for different digits—and so they do, except for Uncle's error.

```
X T M B
W H M W
T T M W
M X M B
─────────
B B B B
═════════
```

Which letter is wrong? What should it be?
Write out the correct addition sum.

# PART VII

## Cross-Number Puzzles

### (43–49)

## 43. Cross-Number Puzzle (3 by 3) (*)

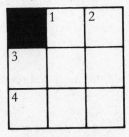

(There are no 0's.)

*Across*

1. The square of 5 across.
4. Each digit is greater than the one before.
5. See 1 across.

*Down*

1. The digits are all even, and each one is less than the one before.
2. Odd; the sum of the digits is 18.
3. The digits are different, and their sum is 10.

## 44. Cross-Number Puzzle (3 by 3) (*)

(There are no 0's.)

*Across*

1. Half of 2 down.
3. Each digit is 2 greater than the one before.

65

4. The sum of the digits is at least 3 greater than the sum of the digits of 1 across.

*Down*
1. The first digit is greater than the second digit by the same amount as the second digit is greater than the third digit.
2. Twice 1 across.
3. An odd number.

## 45. Cross-Number Puzzle (5 by 5) (**)

(There are no 0's.)

*Across*
1. The sum of the digits is 12.
3. A prime number.
5. Each digit is greater than the one before.
7. The digits are all even and different; they are in either ascending or descending order.
8. The digits are all odd and all different.
9. The sum of the digits is less than the sum of the digits of 1 across.
10. A multiple of 2 primes.

1. A multiple of the cube root of 6 down.
2. The sum of the digits is 24.
3. The square of a number, followed by the number itself.
4. The same when reversed.
6. A perfect cube.
8. Even.

## 46. Cross-Number Puzzle (5 by 5) (***)

(There are no 0's.)

*Across*

1. 5 down multiplied by an even number.
3. A multiple of 6 down.
6. A perfect square.
7. The first digit of this number appears 3 times in this puzzle.
8. The same when reversed.
9. The digits are all even, and all different.

*Down*

1. Each digit is greater than the one before.
2. Each digit is greater than the one before.
4. The same when reversed.
5. A multiple of the last 2 figures of 9 across reversed.
6. A multiple of 6 across.

# 47. Cross-Number Puzzle (5 by 5) (****)

| 1 | 2 | 3 | | 4 |
|---|---|---|---|---|
| ■ | 5 | | ■ | |
| 6 | | ■ | 7 | |
| 8 | | 9 | 10 | |
| 11 | | | | ■ |

(There is only one 0.)

*Across*

1. The same when reversed; the sum of the digits is 24.
5. See 4 down.
6. A multiple of 19.
7. The sum of the digits is less than the sum of the digits of 10 across.
8. An even number; the sum of the digits is 18.
10. See 7 across.
11. The digits are all odd.

*Down*

2. Each digit is greater than the one before.
3. A factor of the last 2 digits of 11 across.
4. A multiple of the square of 5 across.
6. A perfect cube.
7. The first 3 digits of 2 down rearranged.
9. A multiple of the number formed by the first and last digits of 2 down.

68

# 48. Cross-Number Puzzle
## (5 by 5, with One Clue Incorrect) (****)

(There are no 0's.)

One of the clues that follow is incorrect. Which one? Find the correct solution.

*Across*

1. The digits are all different, and all greater than 4.
6. The number formed by the first 3 digits is a multiple of the number formed by the last 2.
7. A multiple of 3 and of 7.
8. The sum of the digits is the same as the sum of the digits of 11 down.
10. A multiple of 3.
12. A square of a number, followed by the cube of the same number.

*Down*

1. The digits are all different, and either all odd or all even.
2. A prime number.
3. Odd; the sum of the digits is 16.
4. The digits descend and are alternately even and odd or odd and even.
5. The first 2 digits of 4 down reversed.
9. A multiple of the middle digit of 4 down.
11. Even; the sum of the digits is 12.

# 49. Cross-Number Puzzle
# (5 by 5, with One Clue Incorrect) (****)

(There are no 0's.)

One of the clues that follow is incorrect. Which one? Find the correct solution.

*Across*

1. The digits are all odd, and each one is greater than the one before.
5. The digits are alternately odd and even or even and odd, and each one is greater than the one before.
7. A perfect cube.
8. A prime number when reversed.
9. The same when reversed.
11. The digits are all different. The sum of the first 2 digits is twice the sum of the last 2.

*Down*

2. Each digit is greater than the one before.
3. Each digit is less than the one before.
4. The square of a prime number.
5. The sum of the digits is 12.
6. A multiple of 19.
10. An odd multiple of 13.

# PART VIII

## Division:
## Letters for Digits

(50–54)

## 50. Five Digits Divided by Two Digits (*)

In the following division sum each letter stands for a different digit. Rewrite the sum with the letters replaced by digits.

```
              a  t  p
        ─────────────────
  y h ) h  m  m  x  m
        h  x  d
        ─────────
              k  x  m
              h  p  x
              ─────────
                 k  x
                 ════
```

## 51. Five Digits Divided by Two Digits (***)

In this division sum each letter stands for a different digit. Rewrite the sum with the letters replaced by digits.

```
              a  l  x  j
        ───────────────────
  l  x ) j  b  q  x  j
        s  j
        ─────
           x  q
           d  l
           ─────
              h  s  x
              h  d  x
              ─────────
                 l  y  j
                 l  y  j
                 ══════
```

# 52. Six Digits Divided by Three Digits (****)

In this division sum each letter stands for a different digit. Rewrite the sum with the letters replaced by digits.

$$
\begin{array}{r}
\phantom{pec)\,}a\;e\;m\;d \\
p\;e\;c\,\overline{)\,l\;e\;d\;g\;a\;h} \\
c\;l\;d\phantom{\;g\;a\;h} \\
\hline
p\;c\;b\;g\phantom{\;h} \\
p\;a\;p\;p\phantom{\;h} \\
\hline
h\;e\;a\phantom{\;h} \\
g\;d\;m\phantom{\;h} \\
\hline
p\;b\;e\;h \\
p\;b\;c\;g \\
\hline
l\;p
\end{array}
$$

# 53. Uncle Bungle Relapses (***)

In the division sums that Uncle Bungle has made up with letters substituted for digits he has somehow, rather mysteriously, managed to avoid making any errors so far. But to those who know him well, as I do, it was obvious that this was something that could not be expected to last. I'm afraid I have to report that error has now reared its ugly head. In the following division sum one of the letters is incorrect on one of the occasions on which it appears—if it appears more than once.

$$
\begin{array}{r}
u\ d\ h\ t \\
m\,d\,\overline{)\,t\ t\ u\ r\ r} \\
r\ p \\
\hline
g\ d\ u \\
g\ u\ t \\
\hline
d\ r\ r \\
d\ r\ t \\
\hline
g \\
=
\end{array}
$$

What can you say about the letter that is wrong?
Write out the correct sum with the letters replaced by digits.

# 54. An Error Again (****)

He could not keep it up (Uncle Bungle, I mean).

Once more, in the following puzzle (a division sum with letters standing for different digits), error has crept in. *One* letter is wrong on one of the occasions when it appears.

Find the incorrect letter and rewrite the sum with the letters replaced by digits.

```
                    g k q h
        h g ) c g m p i c
              e q d
              ─────
                g g p
                e h m
                ─────
                  h p i
                  d d d
                  ─────
                    k e c
                    k p i
                    ─────
                      k
                      =
```

# PART IX

## The Island of Imperfection

### (55–70)

# 55.  Douggie Was Dumb (*)

During the time when we were shipwrecked on the Island of Imperfection it became necessary for the workers in Our Factory to become well acquainted with the strict rules of the Island's inhabitants.

There are 3 tribes on the Island: the Pukkas, who always tell the truth; the Wotta-Woppas, who never tell the truth; and the Shilli-Shallas, who make statements that are alternately true and false or false and true. This story deals with Charlie, Douggie, and Ernie, who all belong to different tribes.

In some ways we may not have learned much since the cruel sea deposited us here, but "when in Rome," as I have always said, and so I can be relied upon to see that each of us has exactly the amount of imperfection that the rules of the Island require.

Statements are made as follows:

CHARLIE:  I am not a Pukka.
ERNIE:    I am not a Shilli-Shalla.

To which tribe does each of the 3 belong?

# 56. The Un-Flats (**)

On the Island of Imperfection very little is as it should be, and even the new flats that have recently been constructed aren't—hence, they are called the un-flats.

There are three tribes on the Island: the Pukkas, who always tell the truth; the Wotta-Woppas, who never tell the truth; and the Shilli-Shallas, who make statements that are alternately true and false or false and true. We are concerned with 3 inhabitants of the Island, one from each tribe, who each live in one of the 30 un-flats. Numbers 11–20 are reserved for the Shilli-Shallas, numbers 1–10 for one of the other 2 tribes, and numbers 21–30 for the third tribe.

The 3 with whom this story deals have acquired from their dwellings certain physical characteristics that are reflected in their names: They are called Askew, Bent, and Crooked (in no particular order). They each make 2 statements—in accordance, of course, with their tribal characteristics—as follows:

ASKEW:    1. The number of my flat is a multiple of 4.
          2. Bent lives in flat number 7.
BENT:     1. Askew's number is a multiple of 12.
          2. The Shilli-Shalla's number is not a multiple of 6.
CROOKED:  1. I live in flat number 18.
          2. The number of Askew's flat is even.

Find to which tribe each of the 3 belongs and the numbers of their flats.

# 57. Ages and Wages (**)

On the Island of Imperfection there are 3 tribes: the Pukkas, who always tell the truth; the Wotta-Woppas, who never tell the truth; and the Shilli-Shallas, who make statements that are alternately true and false or false and true. This story deals with the ages and wages of 3 inhabitants of the Island, one from each tribe.

The weekly wages of these 3 are all different, and each is an exact number of hopes (the currency of the Island).

Their ages are also different, and no one's weekly wages in hopes are equal to his age. The ages and the weekly wages are all between 24 and 41 inclusive.

The 3 make statements as follows:

A:  1. My wages are greater than my age.
　　2. B's wages are halfway between A's and C's ages.
　　3. My wages are a multiple of 6.
B:  1. A's age is under 35.
　　2. My age is greater than C's.
　　3. C is a Pukka.
　　4. A is a Wotta-Woppa.
C:  1. My age is a multiple of 5.
　　2. A's wages are a multiple of 7.
　　3. B's age is equal to my wages.

Find the tribes to which A, B, and C belong, and also their ages and wages.

# 58. Crooked Crescent (**)

On the Island of Imperfection there are 3 tribes: the Pukkas, who always tell the truth; the Wotta-Woppas, who never tell the truth; and the Shilli-Shallas, who make statements that are alternately true and false or false and true.

Three inhabitants of the Island, one from each tribe (we shall call them A, B, and C, in no particular order), live in 3 different houses on Crooked Crescent, which has houses numbered from 1 to 10 inclusive.

The Pukkas and the Shilli-Shallas live in houses whose numbers are primes, but the Wotta-Woppa does not.

They make statements—in accordance, of course, with their tribal characteristics—as follows:

A: 1. My number is 3 greater than B's.
   2. The difference between B's number and C's is 1.
B: 1. C's first remark is false.
   2. The number of my house is 5.
C: 1. A's second remark is true.
   2. A's number is 7.

Find their tribes and the numbers of their houses.

# 59.  Ladies on the Island (**)

Our isle, we must admit, has never been
A perfect place giving all men a scene
Of what life ought to be. And women too,
That they should have that scene is something new.
  We do our best, and I will tell you now
  About three ladies, where they lived and how,
  Each one is found in the appropriate file
  According to her status on the isle.
By which I mean, one is a Wotta-Woppa;
She always lies, try as one may to stop her.
The Table of Truth of one has stuck a
Little bit. They call this girl a Pukka;
No lies for her. She's found her own Valhalla,
Temple of fame, that is, unlike the Shilli-Shalla,
Who wants to please, and so although her utterances are few,
They are arranged one true, one false, or else one false, one true.
  What do they say? We'll have to see,
  But first we'll call them A, B, C.

A: 1. C's a Pukka; she'll surely go to heaven.
   2. To which I add, the Pukka's number's seven.
   3. Multiply nine by one or more to get one more abode,
      The Shilli-Shalla lives there. What's her number
      on the road?
B: 1. No Wotta-Woppa I; and be quite sure
   2. The house I live in is not number four.
   3. C's never told the truth, nor will until
      The final judgment comes and all is still.
C: 1. Is A a Wotta-Woppa? No, not she.
   2. The number of my house? Not ten plus three.
   3. The Pukka's number? Add the other two,
      And what you want will certainly accrue.

Find the tribe to which A, B, and C belong and the numbers
of their houses. (There are 30 houses on the street.)

# 60. Pay Claims (***)

We have recently started to build up a modern society on the Island of Imperfection. We have come to realize some of the inestimable advantages that a pay claim, with all its color and friendly disagreements, can bring to life.

There are 3 tribes on the Island: the Pukkas, who always tell the truth; the Wotta-Woppas, who never tell the truth; and the Shilli-Shallas, who make statements that are alternately true and false or false and true. Our story deals with one representative from each tribe.

Psychologists of the future may learn much about thinking on the Island at this time from the simple fact that the main units of currency were called hopes, and that a hope was made up of 100 fears.

The 3 representatives (A, B, and C) speak of their tribes and wages as follows:

A: 1. My wages are greater than B's.
    2. The weekly bill for wages (of A, B, and C) is 80 hopes.
    3. C is a Shilli-Shalla.
B: 1. A is a Pukka.
    2. A's wages are 6 hopes less than mine.
    3. The weekly bill for wages (of A, B, and C) is 92 hopes.
C: 1. C's wages are not a multiple of 5 hopes.
    2. A's wages are 9 hopes greater than mine.

(Their wages are all between 20 and 35 hopes per week, inclusive, and in each case they are exact multiples of 50 fears.)

Find each man's tribe and his weekly wage.

# 61. Clubs for the Boys (***)

On the Island of Imperfection there are 3 tribes: the Pukkas, who always tell the truth; the Wotta-Woppas, who never tell the truth; and the Shilla-Shallas, who make statements that are alternately true and false or false and true.

The recent worldwide advances in education and in the standard of living have found their way even to the Island of Imperfection. One of the consequences of this fact has been a sudden proliferation of clubs for gentlemen only, clubs that serve a variety of purposes. The clubs with which this story deals are the Richer Quicker Club, the Happiness Is All Club, the Help Yourselves Club, and the Up and Over Club. It is easy to see what the first 3 are interested in, but the purposes and interests of the fourth remain somewhat obscure.

Three inhabitants of the Island—whom we shall call A, B, and C—each belong, of course, to one of the 3 tribes. They also belong to 3 different clubs.

They make statements as follows:

A: 1. B belongs to the Happiness Is All Club.
   2. None of us belongs to the Richer Quicker Club.
   3. C is a Pukka.
B: 1. C makes more true statements than I do.
   2. A belongs to the Up and Over Club.
   3. A does not belong to the Help Yourselves Club.
C: 1. I belong to the Help Yourselves Club.
   2. I do not belong to the Up and Over Club.
   3. I am a Shilli-Shalla.

Find the tribes and the clubs to which A, B, and C belong.

85

# 62. Tribal Merging (***)

It has recently become an important part of policy on the Island of Imperfection to try to merge all races, tribes, and creeds. (There are 3 tribes on the island: the Pukkas, who always tell the truth; the Wotta-Woppas, who never tell the truth; and the Shilli-Shallas, who make statements that are alternately true and false or false and true.)

It was symbolic of the new trend that 3 friends of mine, though their tribes were all different, should live in the new synthetic wigwams that have recently been built on the block number 30–40 inclusive (each of them, of course, at a different number). It is a curious coincidence that the most truthful of the 3 lives in the wigwam with the highest number of the 3 and the least truthful in that with the lowest number.

These 3 friends represent a nice blend of those who recommended merging, those who very much needed to merge, and those who had already tasted the pleasures and advantages of merging. Their names are Mingle, Single, and Tingle.

They speak as follows:

MINGLE: 1. Tingle's number is a multiple of 8.
2. The difference between my number and that of Single is 6.
SINGLE: 1. Mingle said yesterday that Tingle was a Pukka.
2. I am a Shilli-Shalla.
TINGLE: 1. Mingle's number is not a prime.
2. Single's number is larger than mine.

Find to which tribe each of them belongs and the numbers of their wigwams.

# 63. Emblems Are Out (***)

On the Island of Imperfection there are 3 tribes: the Pukkas, who always tell the truth; the Wotta-Woppas, who never tell the truth; and the Shilli-Shallas, who make statements that are alternately true and false or false and true.

In the old days it was easy to distinguish among these tribes because they all wore their tribal emblems. But things are very slack now; you can't tell a Wotta-Woppa from a Shilli-Shalla, and some of us are afraid that other essential standards may be on the way out. So far, however, whatever the islanders may look like, they have not yet departed from their age-old tribal habits. Yet I'm afraid that I can give no information about the tribes of the 3 inhabitants of the Island with which this story is concerned.

These 3, whom I shall call A, B, and C, live in different houses on the same street, which has houses numbered from 10 to 55 inclusive.

They speak as follows:

A: 1. A's number is greater than B's.
    2. My number is a multiple of 8.
    3. C's third remark is true.
B: 1. A is not a Wotta-Woppa.
    2. C's number is twice a prime.
    3. A makes the same number of true statements as I do.
C: 1. A is not a Shilli-Shalla.
    2. B's second remark is true.
    3. If C's number is reversed, it has no prime factors other than 2.
    4. B's number is greater than C's.

Find the tribes to which A, B, and C belong and discover as much as you can about the numbers of their houses.

# 64. Imperfect Telephone Numbers (****)

They have started to move with the times on the Island of Imperfection, and most residents of the Island now have telephones. But since there are not many people there, it has been possible to arrange for each telephone number to consist of only 2 figures, thus greatly reducing the possibility of wrong numbers.

There are 3 tribes on the island: the Pukkas, who always tell the truth; the Wotta-Woppas, who never tell the truth; and the Shilli-Shallas, who make statements that are alternately true and false or false and true. This story concerns 3 inhabitants of the Island, whom I shall call A, B, and C. I am afraid I can give no information about the tribes to which they belong. There is a lot of mingling these days and perhaps this is a good thing, but for whatever reasons, though members of different tribes may live on the same street, there is no mingling as far as their telephone numbers are concerned; the principles of separateness still apply there. One tribe has the telephone numbers from 10 to 39 inclusive, another the numbers from 40 to 69 inclusive, and the third the numbers from 70 to 99 inclusive.

The 3 inhabitants make statements as follows:

A: 1. B belongs to a more truthful tribe than I do.
   2. B's number is a multiple of 13.
   3. The Shilli-Shallas' numbers are 10 to 39.
B: 1. At least one of us is not a Pukka.
   2. C is a Pukka.
   3. A's number is 24 less than mine.
   4. C's number is greater than A's.
C: 1. The difference between 2 of our numbers is not 2.
   2. A is a Wotta-Woppa.
   3. The Pukkas' numbers are 70 to 99.

What can you say about the tribes and the telephone numbers of A, B, and C?

# 65. The Older, the Truer (****)

On the Island of Imperfection there are 3 tribes: the Pukkas, who always tell the truth; the Wotta-Woppas, who never tell the truth; and the Shilli-Shallas, who make statements that are alternately true and false or false and true.

It has been noticed lately that the passing of the years seems to have brought about in many people a change of heart, resulting very often in an application for a change of tribe. It is known that permission for these changes is not given lightly, but the general trend can be seen from the fact that in a tribal test for which I was recently responsible, among the 3 people taking the test (who are all between the ages of 20 and 40 inclusive) the older a person was, the more truthful was his tribe.

The 3 people (one from each tribe) made remarks as follows:

A: 1. One of our ages is halfway between the ages of the other 2.
   2. B was lying when he said that C was a Shilli-Shalla.
B: 1. A's age is not a prime number.
   2. A is older than I am.
C: 1. A's age is a multiple of 5.
   2. The difference between A's and B's ages is less than 8.

To which tribe do A, B, and C belong, and what are their ages?

# 66. Top Teams Only (****)

Soccer has been played sporadically on the Island of Imperfection for a long time, but lately there has been a new wave of enthusiasm, and there has been great competition to get into the top teams of the 3 tribes who inhabit the Island. These 3 tribes are the Pukkas, who always tell the truth; the Wotta-Woppas, who never tell the truth; and the Shilli-Shallas, who make statements that are alternately true and false or false and true.

We will call the teams A, B, and C. Each team is to play each of the others once, and when some—or perhaps all—the matches have been played the secretary of each team is asked to write down the numbers of matches played, won, lost, and drawn and the goals for and against. They do this, of course, in accordance with their tribal rules: The Pukkas' secretary's numbers are all correct; the Wotta-Woppas' secretary's numbers are all incorrect; and the Shilli-Shallas' secretary's numbers are alternately true and false or false and true. In every case in which a number is incorrect it differs by only 1 from the correct figure.

The table of results thus produced reads as follows:

|   | Played | Won | Lost | Drawn | Goals for | Goals against | Points |
|---|--------|-----|------|-------|-----------|---------------|--------|
| A | 1 | 0 | 0 | 1 | 2 | 3 | 1 |
| B | 2 | 1 | 0 | 1 | 3 | 1 | 3 |
| C | 2 | 1 | 1 | 0 | 3 | 3 | 1 |

Find the score in each match and the tribes to which A, B, and C belong.

# 67.  A Shilli-Shalla at Heart (****)

Ever since his first visit to the Island of Imperfection, Uncle Bungle has thought of himself as a Shilli-Shalla at heart. (There are 3 tribes on the Island: the Pukkas, who always tell the truth; the Wotta-Woppas, who never tell the truth; and the Shilli-Shallas, who make statements that are alternately true and false or false and true.) After much negotiation my Uncle has at least persuaded the authorities to let him take another tribal test.

Three of the leading tribal testers, who prefer to remain anonymous—we shall call them A, B, and C—have agreed to help administer the test, in which 3 remarks, which should accord with the Shilli-Shallas' characteristics, are to be made independently to each of the testers. (The fact that they are to be made *independently* implies that if, for example, Uncle Bungle's last remark to A is false, his first remark to B may be true or false, and so on.)

Uncle Bungle's remarks are as follows:

To A: 1. My wife's name is Jennifer.
      2. My second remark to B will be false.
      3. My third remark to C will be true.
To B: 1. The number of my house is less than 50.
      2. My wife's name is Dora.
      3. The number of my house is odd.
To C: 1. The sum of the digits of the number of my house
         is even.
      2. The number of my house is a multiple of 8.
      3. I have certainly behaved like a perfect Shilli-
         Shalla in my remarks to A.

Uncle Bungle's temporary residence in Rotten Row (which has houses numbered from 1 to 95) is not, I'm afraid, a very satisfactory one; indeed, his wish to qualify for a Shilli-Shalla Shack is partly responsible for his desire to join the tribe.

My Uncle married at rather an advanced age, and I have not in fact met his wife; but I know that her name is either Jennifer or Dora.

It is sad to have to record that Uncle Bungle failed his test, but by the narrowest of margins. If the truthfulness of *one* remark had been changed—from true to false or from false to true—he would have qualified as a Shilli-Shalla.

Which remark failed him? What is his wife's name? What can you say about the number of his house?

# 68. New Arrivals on the Island (****)

Three inhabitants of our little village, whom we shall call X, Y, and Z, set out recently on a cruise around the world. On the way they were shipwrecked on the Island of Imperfection. On this fabulous Island men and women pass their time happily as they did in the golden days; the grass is greener and prices don't keep going up. Its imperfection lies in a little matter of truth telling. There are 3 tribes on the Island: the Pukkas, who always tell the truth; the Wotta-Woppas, who never tell the truth; and the Shilli-Shallas, who make statements that are alternately true and false or false and true.

The authorities insisted that each of the new arrivals should join a different tribe and that each of them should have a tribal number. The Pukka is to have a number between 1 and 10, the Shilli-Shalla a number between 11 and 20, and the Wotta-Woppa a number between 21 and 30 (in each case inclusive).

The 3 inhabitants are naturally anxious to practice their tribal rules, and they make statements as follows:

X: 1. My number is a multiple of 4.
   2. Y's number is less than Z's by 11.
Y: 1. Z's number is even.
   2. Z is a Pukka.
Z: 1. X's number is a multiple of 8.
   2. Y's number is a prime (i.e., it has no factors except itself and 1).

Find X, Y, and Z's numbers.

# 69. Ugly, Stupid, and Toothless (****)

The ways in which the inhabitants of the Island of Imperfection are not what they might be are many and varied. This story deals with 3 of them, whose names are Ugly, Stupid, and Toothless, and one need say no more.

There are 3 tribes on the Island: the Pukkas, who always tell the truth; the Wotta-Woppas, who never tell the truth; and the Shilli-Shallas, who make statements that are alternately true and false or false and true. Ugly, Stupid, and Toothless are engaged, as so often happens on the Island, in a conversation with each other in which they are exercising their tribal characteristics (and indeed, with all the training they have had they cannot do otherwise). It is only recently that they have begun to receive wages for whatever work (or nonwork) they do. The main unit of currency on the Island is called a hope. If a man is a Pukka he will receive wages of 10 to 19 hopes a week. If he is a Shilli-Shalla his wages will be anywhere between 20 and 29 hopes a week. And Wotta-Woppas receive wages that are between 30 and 39 hopes a week. In every case these wages are inclusive, and the workers all get an exact number of hopes per week. I'm afraid it is not possible to give any information as to whether they each belong to a different tribe or all belong to the same tribe, or whether there are 2 from one tribe and 1 from another.

Our 3 friends make statements anonymously as follows:

A: 1. B is a Wotta-Woppa.
   2. My wages are 25 percent less than 20 percent more than one of the others'.
   3. I get 10 hopes more than B.
B: 1. The wages of one of us are not the same as the sum of the wages of the other 2.
   2. We all belong to the same tribe.
   3. Of the 3 statements made by C and by me, more of C's are true than of mine.

C: 1. Ugly gets more than Toothless.
   2. The wages of one of us are 15 percent less than the wages of another.
   3. Stupid is a Shilli-Shalla.

Find out as much as you can about the 3 inhabitants' tribes' wages and names.

# 70. Uncle Bungle Looks at the Family Tree (****)

Uncle Bungle has been doing some traveling recently, and he was very interested to discover some relatives of his—in fact a new lot of Bungles—on the Island of Imperfection.

There are 3 basic tribes on the Island: the Pukkas, who always tell the truth; the Wotta-Woppas, who never tell the truth; and the Shilli-Shallas, who make statements that are alternately true and false or false and true. But there has been so much intermarriage among the tribes that we now have Shilli-Shallas who are the result of a union between a Pukka and a Wotta-Woppa (and they, of course, follow the usual rules for Shilli-Shallas), a Pukka-Shilli-Shalla who makes 2 true statements followed by a false one, and a Wotta-Woppa-Shilli-Shalla who makes 2 false statements followed by a true one. Clearly the situation could get more complicated than this, but I am glad to say that this does not happen in the story with which we are now concerned.

This story is about 4 Bungles, whose names are Clarence, Dimble, Evelyn, and Fresco (these 4 names are used on the Island for either males or females). I am able to tell you that at least one of these 4 is a Pukka, at least one is a Wotta-Woppa, and at least one is a Shilli-Shalla of one kind or another, but I am afraid I can give no information about the tribe of the fourth.

They make statements as follows:

CLARENCE: 1. Fresco is my son.
2. Fresco is a Wotta-Woppa.
3. I am not Dimble's father.

DIMBLE: 1. I am a Shilli-Shalla.
2. More of Clarence's statements are true than of mine.
3. Fresco is not my nephew or niece.

EVELYN:  1. I have no sons or daughters.
         2. Dimble is my father.
         3. Clarence is a Pukka.
FRESCO:  1. Evelyn is my son.
         2. Evelyn has no sons or daughters.
         3. Only one of us is a Pukka.

Find out as much as you can about the tribes to which these 4 Bungles belong, and how they are related to each other.

# Solutions

# 1. The Birthweek

The order of D, A, and F's birthdays is F, D, A.

The difference between them must be 1 or 2 days (not more, for then the 6 birthdays could not be on consecutive days), thus

(i) F      (ii) F
    D            —
    A            D
                  —
                  A

If (i), B's birthday must be at least 3 days after F's, so that C's would be at least 3 days before F's. But the 3 birthdays would then cover 7 days, not 6.

If (ii), B's birthday must be 1 or 3 days (or more) after F's. If 3, C's birthday would be 3 days before F's, and the birthdays would then cover more than 6 days.

∴ B's birthday must be 1 day after F's and C's 1 day before, and E's must be between D's and A's.

*Complete Solution*

    Alf's birthday is on a Sunday.
    Bert's birthday is on a Thursday.
    Charlie's birthday is on a Tuesday.
    Douggie's birthday is on a Friday.
    Ernie's birthday is on a Saturday.
    Fred's birthday is on a Wednesday.

# 2. Today and Today and Today

Put in positive form which day of the week each person says it is, thus:

A: Sunday, Monday.
B: Saturday.
C: Tuesday, Wednesday, Thursday, Friday.
D: Sunday.
E: Tuesday, Wednesday, Thursday.
F: Friday.
G: Monday.

Each day of the week is mentioned, but the only one that is mentioned only *once* is Saturday.

*Complete Solution*

Bert's remark is true: it is Saturday.

# 3. "I Would If I Could"

Denote Uncle's overdraft by U.

Denote Auntie's overdraft by A.

Denote my overdraft by M.

Then:

(i) $U = 63 + M$.

(ii) $A + M = 210$.

(iii) $A = 3U$ (or nearly so; let us suppose that $A = 3U$ exactly).

(iv) From (ii) and (iii), $3U + M = 210$.

(v) And from (i), $U - M = 63$.

Add iv and v: $4U = 273$.

$$\therefore U = \frac{273}{4} = 68\tfrac{1}{4}.$$

$\therefore$ from (iii), $A = 3 \times 68\tfrac{1}{4} = 204\tfrac{3}{4}$, and from (ii), $M = 210 - 204\tfrac{3}{4} = 5\tfrac{1}{4}$.

Suppose $U = 68$.

Then from (i), $M = 5$, and from (ii), $A + 5 = 210$; $\therefore A = 205$.

$$\therefore \frac{A}{U} = \frac{205}{68} = 3\tfrac{1}{68}$$

(vi) If U were 67, then $M = 4$ and $A = 206$;

$$\therefore \frac{A}{U} = \frac{206}{67} = 3\tfrac{5}{67}.$$

If U were 69, then $M = 6$ and $A = 204$; $\therefore \dfrac{A}{U} = \dfrac{204}{69} = 2\tfrac{66}{69}$.

$\therefore$ in neither of these is $\dfrac{A}{U}$ as "near to three as it can be."

And it is easy to see that if U were further away from 68 on either side the situation would be worse.

*Complete Solution*

Auntie's overdraft = £205.
Uncle's overdraft = £68.
My overdraft = £5.

# 4. Rotten Row

(i) B said that his number was 10 more than D's. D said that his number was 5 more than E's. If these are both true, B's number is 15 more than E's. E said that his number was $\frac{1}{3}$ of B's. If this is true, then if B's number is $3x$, E's number is $x$;

$$\therefore B - E = 3x - x = 2x.$$

$\therefore$ B $-$ E must be even. But from above, B $-$ E $= 15$, and this is not possible. $\therefore$ *either* B's remark *or* D's remark *or* E's remark is false. $\therefore$ all the other remarks are true.

(ii) Consider A's and F's remarks (both true). A's number is 6 more than F's, and A's number is twice F's. $\therefore$ F's number must be 6 and A's number must be 12.

(iii) From C's remark, C's number is 9. And from G's remark, G's number is 15, and from H's remark, H's number is 24.

(iv) Consider E's remark, "My number is $\frac{1}{3}$ of B's." If E's number was 2, then B's would be 6; but F's number is 6. If E's number was 3, then B's would be 9; but C's number is 9. If E's number was 4, then B's would be 12; but A's number is 12. If E's number was 5, then B's would be 15; but G's number is 15. E's number cannot be 6, for F's number is 6. We are told that number 7 is not occupied. If E's number was 8, then B's would be 24; but H's number is 24. E's number cannot be 9, for C's number is 9.

$\therefore$ E's number would have to be 10 or more, but in this case it is not possible for E's number to be $\frac{1}{3}$ of B's (there is no number after 29). $\therefore$ E's remark cannot be true. $\therefore$ B's and D's remarks are both true.

(v) From B's and D's remarks B $>$ D $>$ E. $\therefore$ B's number must be 29 (no one else's can be). $\therefore$ D's number (10 less) is 19 and E's number (5 less than D's) is 14.

*Complete Solution*

E's remark is false.

The numbers of the houses are as follows

A 12
B 29
C 9
D 19
E 14
F 6
G 15
H 24

# 5. The Alternate Lie Drug

(i) For Dr. T to claim to know the number of O's house he must obviously think it is a perfect square (there are too many possibilities otherwise). The perfect squares between 10 and 90 are 16, 25, 36, 49, 64, and 81. And of these, 2 (36 and 81) are also multiples of 3. The only way it is possible for Dr. T to claim to know the number of O's house is for him (Dr. T) to live in *either* 36 *or* 81, and to think that O lives in the other.

(ii) Dr. S thinks he knows the number of O's house. His information is that it does or does not end in 1, that it is or is not a prime number, that it is not the same as his own, and that it is not the same as Dr. T's (which is either 36 or 81—Dr. S knows which, even though we do not yet). For Dr. S to have reduced the possibilities to only one, he must clearly think that the number ends in 1 and therefore that it is 11, 21, 31, 41, 51, 61, 71, or 81. Of these, 11, 31, 41, 61, and 71 are primes and 21, 51, and 81 are not. The only way Dr. S can claim to know the number of O's house is if 81 is the number announced by Dr. T (we know that this number is either 36 or 81) and if his (Dr. S's) number is either 21 or 51. He then thinks that O's number is the other.

(iii) We know that O's number differs from either Dr. T's or Dr. S's by 26. We also know that his number does not end in 1 and that it is a prime. (What Dr. S thought about the truthfulness of the answers to his questions was incorrect. What Dr. T thought about the answers to his questions was also incorrect, but this does not give us any more information than that it is a prime number.) 81 + 26 is too large; 81 − 26 = 55, not a prime. 51 + 26 = 77, not a prime; 51 − 26 = 25, not a prime. But 21 + 26 = 47, and this is a prime number. ∴ this is O's number, and this also tells us that Dr. S's number must be 21 and not 51.

*Complete Solution*

Dr. Try's number is 81.
Dr. See's number is 21.
Orders's number is 47.

# 6. Dothemens Hall

(i) Consider P2. If this is false, then Q's grade is A or B. Consider R1. If this is false, R's grade is D, E, O, or F. Consider S2. If this is false, Q's grade is lower than R's (it cannot be equal); i.e., Q's grade is E, O, or F. But it is not possible for Q's grade to be A or B *and* to be E, O, or F. ∴ these 3 statements (P2, R1, and S2) cannot all be false; ∴ one of them must be true. ∴ all the other remarks made are false.

(ii) From Q1 (false), Q's grade is not A; and from Q2, P's grade is not A, B, or C. ∴ from R2 (false), S's grade is D, E, O, or F. ∴ neither Q, P, nor S got a grade of A. But from P1, someone did; ∴ R got a grade of A.

(iii) We know that only one of P2, R1, S2 is true. But R1 is true. ∴ P2 and S2 are false.

(iv) Since P2 is false, Q's grade is A or B. But it is not A (for R's grade is A); ∴ Q's grade is B.

(v) From R2 (false), S's grade is lower than P's. We know that P's grade is D or lower. ∴ S's grade is E or lower. But from S1, S's grade is E or higher. ∴ S's grade is E. ∴ P's grade is D.

*Complete Solution*

Rachel's first remark was true.
Priscilla's grade is D.
Queenie's grade is B.
Rachel's grade is A.
Susan's grade is E.

# 7. The Factory Accountant

Set out in positive terms, using obvious abbreviations, what each says about the possibilities:

A: P or S
B: R or S
C: Q or R
D: P, R, or S

If P, R, or S is selected, at least 2 of them are right. But if Q is selected, only C is right.

*Complete Solution*

Quick was appointed.

# 8. The Boss's Birthday

Put in positive form the month or months in which each man says the boss's birthday occurs:

A:  March, May, November.
B:  July, August.
C:  October, November, December, January, February.
D:  April, June, September, November.
E:  October.
F:  April, May, June, July, August, September.
G:  January, February, March, April.

If my birthday was in January, C and G statements would both be true. We want, therefore, to look for a month in the preceding list that is mentioned *only once* by my employees, at the same time making sure that every month is mentioned.

In fact every month is mentioned. The only month to be mentioned only once is December, and it is mentioned by C.

*Complete Solution*

Charlie's statement is true. My birthday is in December.

# 9. How to Be Horizontal and First

(i)  Consider E's remark. If this was false, E was last. But the false remark was not made by the person who was last. ∴ E's remark was not false and E was not sixth.

(ii)  Consider B's and F's remarks. We know that E was not sixth, ∴ it is not possible for F to be 2 places ahead of E, and also 3 places behind B. ∴ one of these remarks must be false. ∴ all other remarks are true.

(iii)  ∴ either B or F was first. Suppose F was first, so that F's remark was false. But if F was first, B's remark ("I was 3 places ahead of Fred") is also false. ∴ F cannot be first; ∴ B was first, and his remarks were false; ∴ B was *not* 3 places ahead of F.

(iv)  So far we have the following information.

1 B
2
3
4 *not* F
5
6 *not* E

(v)  From C's remark, A was not last, and from D's remark, A was 2 places behind D. ∴ D was second or third, and A was fourth or fifth.

(vi)  E was not sixth, and since F was 2 places ahead of E (see F's remarks) and was not fourth, F must be second or third. If F was third, then D would be second and A would be fourth. But A was more than one place behind F (see A's remark). ∴ F cannot be third; ∴ F was second, D third, and A fifth. And from F's remark, E was fourth; ∴ C was sixth.

*Complete Solution*

1 Bert
2 Fred
3 Douggie
4 Ernie
5 Alf
6 Charlie

+ Bert was
   incorrect

# 10. Our Factory Has a Holiday Outing

(i) Consider C1. This cannot be true, for it would mean that a W-W made a true statement. ∴ C is not a W-W, but makes a false statement. ∴ C is a Sh-Sh; and C1 is false and C2 is true.

(ii) Consider B1. If this is true, then A is a Pukka, B has made a true statement, and C is a Sh-Sh. ∴ D would have to be a W-W. But we know that D2 is true; ∴ our assumption is false and B1 is not true.

(iii) ∴ A is not a Pukka; ∴ D must be a Pukka (no one else can be). And we know that A2 is true; ∴ A is a Sh-Sh and B must be a W-W.

(iv) A diagram like the following will help:

|  | Door opener | Door shutter | Welfare officer | Bottle washer |  |
|---|---|---|---|---|---|
| Alf |  | X |  |  | Shilli-Shalla |
| Bert |  | X |  |  | Wotta-Woppa |
| Charlie |  | X |  |  | Shilli-Shalla |
| Douggie | X | √ | X | X | Pukka |

From C2 (true), D is the DS (this has been inserted in the diagram; the reader is advised to insert other facts as they are obtained).

(v) From A1 (false), the WO is not a W-W; ∴ the WO is not B. From D1 (true), the DO is a Sh-Sh; ∴ DO is A or C. ∴ B is the BW (no one else can be). From B2 (false), C is not the WO. ∴ C must be the DO and A the WO.

*Complete Solution*

Alf is the welfare officer and is a Shilli-Shalla.
Bert is the bottle washer and is a Wotta-Woppa.
Charlie is the door opener and is a Shilli-Shalla.
Douggie is the door shutter and is a Pukka.

# 11. The Richer, the Truer

(i) Suppose C1 is true. Then A paid more than C and ∴ is more truthful. ∴ both A's remarks are true; ∴ A's wages are a multiple of 7p. ∴ they must be £14.00 or £17.50, but not £14.00, for A would then be least truthful. ∴ B's wages would have to be £14.00 (B is less truthful than C). ∴ B2 would be true. But this is not possible. ∴ our assumption is false. ∴ C1 is false.

(ii) Suppose B1 is true. Then the BW makes 2 false remarks (we know that C makes 1). ∴ the BW is A (we are assuming that B1 is true). And B's remarks are both true and C2 is true. ∴ the DO's wages are £14.50 and the BW's must be £14.00. ∴ A1 is true. But on our assumption, A (the BW) makes 2 false remarks. ∴ our assumption is incorrect. ∴ B1 is false.

(iii) Since B and C have each made a false remark, A's are both true. ∴ A's wages are a multiple of 7p. They cannot be £14.00 (A would then be least truthful). ∴ A's wages are £17.50.

(iv) Consider A2. Suppose the SU is A (wages = £17.50). Then the BW is not C (C1 is false). ∴ the BW is B. ∴ B is paid £14.50 and B2 is false. ∴ C makes one true statement. ∴ C2 is true. But the BW and the DO cannot have the same wages. ∴ our assumption is false and the SU is not A. Suppose the SU is C. Then C's wages must be £17.00 and B's £14.00 (the only way for them both to be less than A and to differ by £3). ∴ B2 is true. But since B's wages are £14.00, both statements are false. ∴ the SU is not C. ∴ the SU is B. ∴ the BW must be C and the DO is A. B's wages must be £17.00 and C's £14.00. (B2 is true and C2 false.)

Alf is the door opener: his wages are £17.50.
Bert is the sweeper-upper: his wages are £17.00.
Charlie is the bottle washer: his wages are £14.00.

# 12. Sharing Power in Our Factory

(i) A is the SU.

(ii) Consider "he who makes tea for eight." We know that the TB is also the WO, but we do not know his name. C is not the DS, and D is not the BW. B is not the W or the DO. D is not the DO, DS, or DP. The information obtained so far can be represented thus:

| | Sweeper-upper | Door opener | Door shutter | Doorknob polisher | Welfare officer | Bottle washer | Tea boy | Worker |
|---|---|---|---|---|---|---|---|---|
| Alf | ✓ | | | | | | | |
| Bert | X | X | | | | | | X |
| Charlie | X | | X | | | | | |
| Douggie | X | X | X | X | | X | | |

(iii) Consider D. His 2 jobs must be 2 of WO, TB, and W. But since the WO must be the TB, D cannot be the W and must be the WO and TB. ∴ either A or C is the W. Suppose C. Then C cannot be the DO ("the opener of the door" is not the worker). ∴ A is the DO (no one else can be). ∴ A is not the DS, DP, or BW. ∴ B is the DS (no one else can be). ∴ B is not the BW ("Nor is the bottle washer he who shuts them," i.e., the doors). ∴ B is the DP (the only job left). ∴ C is the BW. But we are told that W is *not* the BW. But according to our assumption, C is the BW and the W.

∴ our assumption is wrong. ∴ A must be the W. ∴ A is the SU and nothing else. ∴ B is the DS (no one else can be) and C is the DO (no one else can be).

(iv) The BW is not the DS. ∴ B is the DP (the only job left for him). ∴ C is the BW (the only job left for him).

117

Alf is the sweeper-upper and the worker.
Bert is the door shutter and the doorknob polisher.
Charlie is the door opener and the bottle washer.
Douggie is the welfare officer and the tea boy.

# 13. Higher Thinking in Our Factory

(i) Consider question 6. The only way in which a total of 35 can be reached is if A's and C's answers are correct (10 marks each) and the other 3 get 5 marks each.

(ii) Then D got no marks for any other question. ∴ answer D4 (7) gets no mark and is therefore wrong (but note that B might have gotten 5 marks for this answer).

(iii) A got 15 marks, and got 10 for question 6. ∴ all A's other answers are wrong (but he got 5 marks for one of them). ∴ 8 is not the right answer for question 4, and we already know that it is not 7; ∴ it must be 12, and C and E each got 10 marks for this question and all the others got 0.

(iv) Consider question 1. We know that 20 is not the right answer (D got 0 for this question). C got 10 for question 4 and 10 for question 6, but only 25 in all. ∴ C got not more than 5 for question 1. ∴ 18 is not the right answer. ∴ 26 must be the right answer for question 1, and B and E got 10 each.

(v) Consider question 3. A's answer is not right (A has already gotten 10 out of his total of 15); C's answer is not right (C has already gotten 20 out of his total of 25); D's answer is not right (D got *no* question right). ∴ B's and E's answer of 38 must be correct.

(vi) Consider question 2. Only one person got it right (the total for the question was 10); ∴ C's and D's answer of $2.40 is not right. A's answer cannot be right, for A has already gotten 10 out of his 15 marks. D got no questions right. ∴ B's answer of $10.10 must be correct.

(vii) Consider question 5. We know that A, C, and D's answers are wrong (none of them can get another 10 marks). And E has already gotten his total of 35. ∴ B's answer of $110 must be correct.

*Complete Solution*

The correct answers are as follows:

1. 26
2. $10.10
3. 38
4. 12
5. $110
6. 15%

# 14. The End of an Era

It will help to have the data in rather more compact form, thus:

A: I think I beat C.

B: I think I beat E.

C: 1. I think A was above G.

2. I think F was 2 places above me.

D: 1. I think G was above B.

2. I think I was above C.

E: I think B was 3 places above D.

F: I think I was above A.

G: I think D was above A.

(i) From G, D is above A.

(ii) From C1, A is above G.

(iii) From D1, G is above B.

(iv) From E, B is 3 places above D.

But this is not possible; we cannot have D above A, G, and B and also have B above D. ∴ one of these must be wrong. ∴ all other opinions must be correct. ∴ A, B, C2, D2, and F are correct.

(v) From F, F is above A; from A, A is above C; and from C2, F is 2 places above C; ∴ F must be one place above A, who is one place above C. And from D2, D is above C; ∴ D must be above F.

(vi) Suppose that E's remark was true ("B was 3 places above D"). Then we would have the following:

1 B

2

3

4 D

5 F

6 A

7 C

E and G would occupy the two vacant places. But in this case C1 (A is above G) and D1 (G is above B) would *both* be false. But we are told that there is only one false remark; ∴ our assumption was incorrect. ∴ *E's remark was false*; ∴ all other remarks are true.

(vii) ∴ C1 is true (A is above G) and D1 is true (G is above B), and we also have B's remark that B was above E. ∴ we have the following:

1 D
2 F
3 A
4 C
5 G
6 B
7 E


*Complete Solution*
1 Douggie
2 Fred
3 Alf
4 Charlie
5 George
6 Bert
7 Ernie

# 15. When Rules Were Rules and Pounds Were Pounds

A diagram will help. (Work in units of 10 pence; call this $1t$; $\therefore$ wages are between $100t$ and $200t$, inclusive. $M$ stands for multiple; e.g., $m(6)$ means a multiple of 6.)

| | Door opener | Door shutter | Doorknob polisher | Bottle washer | Welfare officer | Wages |
|---|---|---|---|---|---|---|
| Alf | X | X | X | ✓ | X | |
| Bert | X | ✓ | X | X | X | $200t$ |
| Charlie | | X | | X | — | $m(11)$ |
| Douggie | | X | | X | | $m(10)$ worst paid |
| Ernie | | X | X | X | — | $m(6)$ not worst paid |
| wages | | $200t$ | | $189t$ | | |

(i) From rule 3, the BW gets $\frac{105}{100} \times \frac{90}{100} \times B = \frac{21}{20} \times \frac{9}{10} \times B = \frac{189}{200} \times B$. $\therefore \dfrac{BW}{B} = \dfrac{189}{200}$. $\therefore$ B gets $200t$ and the BW gets $189t$. $\therefore$ B is not the BW. And B ($200t$) must be the DS (best paid).

(ii) From rule 6, E gets $\frac{120}{100} \times (DP - 10t) = \frac{6}{5}(x - 10)t$. If E were the DP, then $x = \frac{6}{5}(x - 10)$. $\therefore 5x = 6x - 60$. $\therefore x = 60$. $\therefore$ E's wages are equal to the DP's only if they are both $60t$. But they are not (wages are between $100t$ and $200t$). $\therefore$ E is not the DP. And if the DP's wages $> 60$, then E's wages $>$ the DP's wages. $\therefore$ E is not the worst paid and E's wages are $m(6)$.

(iii) From rule 1, C's wages are $m(11)$ ($\frac{11}{10}$ of the worst-paid employee's wages). $\therefore$ C is not the BW (whose wages are $189t$), and C is not the worst paid; nor is B, nor E. And from rule 2, nor is A. $\therefore$ D is the worst paid; $\therefore$ D's wages are $m(10)$. $\therefore$ D is not the BW (whose wages are $189t$).

122

(iv) E's wages are $m(6)$; $\therefore$ E is not the BW (whose wages are $189t$). $\therefore$ by elimination A is the BW. (The information obtained so far has been inserted in the diagram.)

(v) From rule 5, the DO cannot be D $[m(10)]$ or E $[m(6)]$. $\therefore$ the DO is C. $\therefore$ by elimination D is the DP and E is the WO, and we know the jobs of all of the employees.

(vi) E's wages $= \frac{6}{5}(DP - 10t)$. We know that the DP's wages are $m(10)$; $\therefore$ E $= \frac{6}{5}(m(10) + 10t)$. $\therefore$ E's wages are $m(12)$.

(vii) We now have (from rule 1) $\dfrac{C}{D} = \dfrac{11}{10}$. And from rule 6,

E $= \frac{6}{5}(D - 10)$. And that D is $m(10)$. The possibilities in $t$'s are as follows:

| Douggie | 100 | 110 | 120 | 130 | 140 | 150 | 160 | 170 |
|---|---|---|---|---|---|---|---|---|
| Charlie | 110 | 121 | 132 | 143 | 154 | 165 | 176 | 187 |
| Ernie | 108 | 120 | 132 | 144 | 156 | 168 | 180 | 192 |

But from rule 4, D gets £1 more or £1 less than E. $\therefore$ D must get $110t$. E gets $120t$, and C gets $121t$.

*Solution*

Charlie gets £12.10; Douggie gets £11.00; Ernie gets £12.00.

*Complete Solution*

Alf is the bottle washer and gets £18.90.
Bert is the door shutter and gets £20.00.
Charlie is the door opener and gets £12.10.
Douggie is the doorknob polisher and gets £11.00.
Ernie is the welfare officer and gets £12.00.

123

# 16. Three Teams: All Figures Correct

(i) C drew one match, but had no goals against it. ∴ the score in C's drawn match must have been 0–0, and the score in C's other match was 2–0.

(ii) A lost both matches; ∴ C's drawn match was against B (0–0), and the score of C vs. A was 2–0.

(iii) B scored no goals against C; ∴ B scored 3 goals against A.

(iv) A scored no goals against C; ∴ A scored 2 goals against B.

*Complete Solution*

| | |
|---|---|
| A vs. B | 2–3 |
| A vs. C | 0–2 |
| B vs. C | 0–0 |

# 17. Four Teams: All Figures Correct

(i) The total of matches played must be even, for each match appears twice. C won 3; ∴ C played 3 (no one can play more). ∴ the total of A, B, and C is 8; ∴ D's total must be 0 or 2. But it is not 0, for D scored some goals; ∴ D played 2.

(ii) A and C played all the others; but B and D could not have played each other. A table will help, thus:

|   | A | B | C | D |
|---|---|---|---|---|
| A |   | Drawn | Lost | Drawn |
| B | Drawn |   | Lost |   |
| C | Won | Won |   | Won |
| D | Drawn |   | Lost |   |

C won all 3 matches; ∴ A, B, and D lost to C. We know that B drew a match; this can only be against A (mark this in the diagram). We know that D drew a match; this can only be against A (mark in). We now know the result of each match.

(iii) B scored no goals; ∴ the score of B vs. A (drawn) was 0–0 and that of B vs. C was 0–3.

(iv) C beat D by 2 goals (D's goals were 3–5, and D's other game was drawn). ∴ the score of C vs. D was 3–1 or 2–0 (it is not more than 3, for C scored 3 against B, at least 1 vs. A, and only 7 in all). If the score of D vs. C was 0–2, then that of D vs. A was 3–3. But A scored only 2 goals; ∴ the score of D vs. C cannot have been 0–2, ∴ the score of D vs. C must have been 1–3.

(v) ∴ the score of D vs. A was 2–2. And since C scored only 7 goals, the score of C vs. A was 1–0.

*Complete Solution*

| | |
|---|---|
| A vs. B | 0–0 |
| A vs. C | 0–1 |
| A vs. D | 2–2 |
| B vs. C | 0–3 |
| C vs. D | 3–1 |

# 18. Uncle Bungle Again

(i) The total of goals for all teams must be equal to the total of goals against all teams. ∴ B's goals for are 3.

(ii) Since B's goals for are greater than its goals against, B won at least one match. And since C's goals for are greater than its goals against, C won at least one match. And we know that at least one match was drawn. ∴ 3 matches were played; ∴ the teams all played each other.

(iii) C scored 5 goals against A and B, and A and B *between them* had 6 goals against them. ∴ 1 of these 6 goals was in the match between A and B. But we cannot yet tell whether A or B scored it. (Similarly, C had 4 goals against it, and A and B *between them* scored 5 goals; ∴ again 1 goal was scored in A vs. B.)

(iv) Since we now know that the score of A vs. B is 1–0 or 0–1, and that A's goals are 2 for and 4 against, the score of A vs. C must be 1–4 or 2–3 (to make the total right). Similarly, we can fill in the other possibilities, thus:

|   | A | B | C |
|---|---|---|---|
| A |   | 1–0<br>0–1 | 1–4<br>2–3 |
| B | 0–1<br>1–0 |   | 3–1<br>2–2 |
| C | 4–1<br>3–2 | 1–3<br>2–2 |   |

But we know that at least one match was drawn; and this can only be B vs. C (2–2). ∴ the score of B vs. A must be 1–0 and that of A vs. C must be 2–3.

*Complete Solution*

| A vs. B | 0–1 |
|---|---|
| A vs. C | 2–3 |
| B vs. C | 2–2 |

# 19. The Lie Drug

(i) Since the number of matches won by A was not 0, and the number drawn by B was not 0, and the goals for C were not 0, A, B, and C each played at least one match.

(ii) No team can play more than 2 matches. B has not played 1; ∴ B has played 2.

(iii) A won 1 or 2 (the figure given is 0); ∴ A got at least 2 points. But the figure given for A's points is 2; ∴ A got more than 2 points; ∴ A played 2 matches. ∴ C must have played 2 matches (to make the total even); ∴ they each played each other team.

(iv) A's points must be 3 or 4; B drew at least 1 (the figure given is 0). ∴ B's points are 1, 2, or 3. ∴ A and B between them got at least 4 points. ∴ C did not get more than 2 points (6 points in all). C did not get 0 points (the figure given), and C did not get 1 point (C did not draw 1, the figure given). ∴ C got 2 points, A got 3, and B got 1.

(v) C did not win 1 (the figure given); ∴ C must have drawn 2. ∴ A vs. C and B vs. C were both drawn. And the third match (A vs. B) was won by A (A got 3 points). We now know the result of each match.

(vi) Consider C's goals. The score in each of C's drawn matches was 0–0 or 1–1 (there were not more than 3 goals in any match), but not 0–0 and 0–0 (this would make goals for 0, but they are not). And it was not 0–0 and 1–1 (this would make goals against 1, but they are not). ∴ the scores were 1–1 and 1–1.

(vii) Consider B's goals. B scored one goal against C, but more than one goal in all (the figure given is 1); ∴ the score of B vs A was 1–2 (there is no other possibility).

*Complete Solution*

| | | |
|---|---|---|
| A vs. B | 2–1 | |
| A vs. C | 1–1 | |
| B vs. C | 1–1 | |

# 20. A Diversity of Scores

(i) B scored 2 more than each of the other 3. Suppose the other 3 scored $x$. Then $3x + (x + 2) = 18$; $\therefore 4x = 16$ and $x = 4$.

(ii) A had 4 goals against it (the same as the number of goals for it); B:D is 3:1. If B was 6 or 3 and D was 2 or 1, then C would have scored 8 or more. But C had the smallest number of goals against it; $\therefore$ B is 9, D is 3, and C is 2. Thus:

|   | Goals for | Goals against |
|---|---|---|
| A | 4 | 4 |
| B | 6 | 9 |
| C | 4 | 2 |
| D | 4 | 3 |

(iii) B had 9 goals against it and must therefore have played A, C, and D (2 of them could not have scored more than 8). And as A, C, and D scored 12 goals in all, 9 of them must have been against B and the other 3 against each other. And since only 3 goals were scored, only one other match can have been played (2 matches would mean that at least 4 goals were scored). And the score in this match must be 1–2. (We do not yet know who played in this match.)

(iv) Suppose C played in this other match. Then the score is 2–1, and the score of C's other match (against B) is also 2–1 (see goals total). This is not possible, for the scores of 2 matches must not be the same. $\therefore$ C did not play in the other match; $\therefore$ the other match must have been A vs. D.

(v) A diagram will help.

|   | A | B | C | D |
|---|---|---|---|---|
| A |   | 3–2<br>2–3 |   | 1–2<br>2–1 |
| B | 2–3<br>3–2 |   | 2–4 | 2–2<br>1–3 |
| C |   | 4–2 |   |   |
| D | 2–1<br>1–2 | 2–2 |   |   |

We know that the score of C's one match must be 4–2. And the score of A vs. D is 1–2 or 2–1; ∴ the score of A vs. B is 3–2 or 2–3. And the score of D vs. B is 2–2 or 3–1. But we know that one match was drawn, and this can only be D vs. B. Delete 3–1 in D vs. B, and the *second* score in each square is the correct one.

*Complete Solution*

| A vs. B | 3–2 |
|---------|-----|
| A vs. D | 1–2 |
| B vs. C | 2–4 |
| B vs. D | 2–2 |

# 21. Some Sticky Impedimenta

(i) The figure that is wrong must clearly be found first. If D played 4 (i.e., played everyone), drew 0, and had 0 goals against it, then it must have won all its matches and B cannot have had 0 goals against it. ∴ either "D played" or "D drawn" or "D goals against" or "B goals against" must be wrong. ∴ all other figures are correct.

(ii) C had 1 goal for it and 1 against it and drew 0; ∴ C played only 2 matches (scores: 1–0 and 0–1).

(iii) A had 3 points from 3 matches, but did not draw them all (see goals). ∴ A won 1, lost 1, and drew 1.

(iv) E got only 1 point and ∴ won 0, drew 1, and played 3.

(v) ∴ A, B, C, and E played, respectively, 3, 3, 2, and 3 matches. ∴ D must have played an odd number (1 or 3) to make the total played even. ∴ the other figures are correct, and neither B nor D can have lost a match.

(vi) ∴ we have the following:

|   | Played | Won | Lost | Drawn | Goals for | Goals against | Points |
|---|--------|-----|------|-------|-----------|---------------|--------|
| A | 3 | 1 | 1 | 1 | 2 | 4 | 3 |
| B | 3 | | 0 | | | 0 | |
| C | 2 | 1 | 1 | 0 | 1 | 1 | 2 |
| D | 1 or 3 | | 0 | 0 | | 0 | |
| E | 3 | 0 | 2 | 1 | 1 | | 1 |

(vii) If D played 3, then the total number won would be greater than the total number lost, which is impossible. ∴ D played 1. "D played" is the incorrect figure. It should be 1.

*Complete Solution*

The details of all matches are as follows:

| | | |
|---|---|---|
| A vs. B | 0–0 |
| A vs. D | 0–3 |
| A vs. E | 2–1 |
| B vs. C | 1–0 |
| B vs. E | 0–0 |
| C vs. E | 1–0 |

# 22.  A Subdued Uncle

A won 2 and drew 1 and had 6 goals for and 5 goals against, but this is only possible if they also lost 1.  ∴ A must have played all the others.

We are told that D played all the others.

E lost none and had no goals for, but they got 2 points. This is only possible if they drew 2, with the score in each of them 0–0.

∴ E vs. A was 0–0, and E vs. D was 0–0, and E did not play B or C.

B lost 2 and had 2 goals against but got no points.  ∴ B only played 2 (A and D), and the score in each match was 0–1. And B did not play C.

We know that D drew 2. One of them was vs. E (0–0), and the other was not vs. A (who only drew 1, vs. E), and not vs. B who lost both their matches, and not vs. E (see above).  ∴ D's other drawn match was vs. C. D had 5 goals for and 5 against, drew 2 (vs. C and vs. E) and won 1 vs. B.  ∴ D must have lost their other match vs. A.

∴ since A won vs. B and vs. D and drew vs. E their lost match was vs. C.

*Results so far*

|   | A | B | C | D | E |
|---|---|---|---|---|---|
| **A** | X | W<br>1–0 | L | W | Dr<br>0–0 |
| **B** | L<br>0–1 | X | X | L<br>0–1 | X |
| **C** | W | X | X | Dr | X |
| **D** | L | W<br>1–0 | Dr | X | Dr<br>0–0 |
| **E** | Dr<br>0–0 | X | X | Dr<br>0–0 | X |

B did not score a goal, and E had no goals for or against. ∴ since total of goals for must be equal to total of goals against. C had 9 goals for.

Consider D vs. A, which D lost. Suppose that score was 1–2 (D cannot have lost by more than 1 goal—see the rest of D's figures). Then D vs. C would be 3–3 and C vs. A would be 6–5 (C's goals are 9–8). But this is not possible, for A's goals would then be 8–7 instead of 6–5. And if D vs. A was 2–3 the situation would be even worse. ∴ D vs. A must be 0–1, C vs. D is 4–4, and C vs. A is 5–4.

*Complete Solution*

| | |
|---|---|
| A vs. B | 1–0 |
| A vs. C | 4–5 |
| A vs. D | 1–0 |
| A vs. E | 0–0 |
| B vs. D | 0–1 |
| C vs. D | 4–4 |
| D vs. E | 0–0 |

# 23. The False Drug Fails

(i) Look first for 2 figures that are true. Consider D. If the first 4 figures are all wrong, we could have only the following:

| | Played | Won | Lost | Drawn |
|---|---|---|---|---|
| D | 3 | 1 | 1 | 1 |

And the points would be 3; but the points *are* 3. ∴ *either* D's points *or* one of D's other figures must be correct (or possibly both). If "D Played" is correct and only 2 matches were played, then either "D Won" or "D Lost" or "D Drawn" would also be correct (for D must have either won, lost, or drawn *none*).

(ii) Consider B. If "B Played" is wrong, then it must be 2 or less, and "B Won," "B Lost," and "B Drawn" cannot all be wrong. ∴ there must be one correct figure in B. ∴ there is only one correct figure in D. ∴ "D Played" must be 3 [see (i)]. And A's and C's figures must all be wrong.

(iii) Consider A: 2 or 1 were played, at least 1 drawn.
∴ A did *not* win 2 or lose 2, but 0 is the correct figure. ∴ the figures for A are as follows:

| Played | Won | Lost | Drawn | Points |
|---|---|---|---|---|
| 2 | 0 | 0 | 2 | 2 |

(iv) Consider C. "C Won" and "C Drawn" must be at least 1; ∴ 3 matches were played and not 1. "C Lost" must be 0, and the correct figures must be *either* 2 won, 1 drawn *or* 1 won, 2 drawn. But 2 won, 1 drawn would make the points 5, and the points are given as 5. ∴ the figures for C are as follows:

| Played | Won | Lost | Drawn | Points |
|---|---|---|---|---|
| 3 | 1 | 0 | 2 | 4 |

(v) The numbers of matches played by A, C, and D are 2, 3, 3. ∴ since the total of matches played must be even, B played 2.

∴ we now have as correct figures the following:

|   | Played | Won | Lost | Drawn | Points |
|---|--------|-----|------|-------|--------|
| A | 2 | 0 | 0 | 2 | 2 |
| B | 2 |   |   |   |   |
| C | 3 | 1 | 0 | 2 | 4 |
| D | 3 |   |   |   |   |

(vi) Either "B Won" or "B Lost" or "B Drawn" must be 0 (and ∴ correct); ∴ "B Points" (2) must be incorrect. But if "B Drawn" was 0, "B Points" would be 2. ∴ "B Drawn" cannot be correct; ∴ "B Drawn" is 1 (not 2, for this would make "B Won" and "B Lost" *both* 0, and ∴ correct). And since the total of matches drawn must be even, "D Drawn" must be 1 (not 3, for "D Won" and "D Lost" would then both be correct).

(vii) Suppose B won its other match. Then D must have lost both its other matches (to make total won = total lost). This would give B 3 points and D 1. But we are told that D got more points than B. ∴ B lost its other match. And the table of results looks like this:

|   | A | B | C | D |
|---|---|---|---|---|
| A |   |   | drawn | drawn |
| B |   |   | drawn | lost |
| C | drawn | drawn |   | won |
| D | drawn | won | lost |   |

(Note that as "C Drawn" is 2, B's drawn match must have been against C. And since we know that C got 4 points, C beat D.)

135

(viii) Consider scores. (We know that all these figures are wrong.) The figures for A (2 drawn matches) are 0 goals for and 1 goal against. And since not more than 3 goals were scored in any match, the score of A vs. C was 1–1 and that of A vs. D was 1–1 (anything less would make *either* goals for *or* goals against correct).

(ix) Consider B's goals (the correct figures are *not* 0 goals for and 2 goals against). If the score of B vs. C was 0–0, then that of B vs. D would be either 0–? or 1–2. But neither of these is possible; ∴ the score of B vs. C was 1–1 and that of B vs. D could be 0–2, 0–3, or 1–2.

(x) Consider C's goals (the correct figures are *not* 3 goals for and 2 goals against). C has already gotten 2 goals against it by A and B; ∴ D must have scored at least 1 more; ∴ the score of C vs. D (won) was 2–1.

(xi) Consider D's goals (the correct figures are *not* 4 goals for and 2 goals against). From (ix) the score of D vs. B is 2–0, 2–1, or 3–0. But 2–0 or 2–1 would make goals for 4. ∴ the score of D vs. B was 3–0.


*Complete Solution*

| | |
|---|---|
| A vs. C | 1–1 |
| A vs. D | 1–1 |
| B vs. C | 1–1 |
| B vs. D | 0–3 |
| C vs. D | 2–1 |

# 24. Six Digits Divided by Two Digits

```
                   2 - - - · -        (i)
        - - ) - - 0 - - 1             (ii)
              - -                     (iii)
             _____
              - - -                   (iv)
              - - -                   (v)
             _____
              - - 7                   (vi)
              - - -                   (vii)
             _____
                - - -                 (viii)
                - - -                 (ix)
               ======
```

(viii) and (ix) must be −10; ∴ the divisor must be even or must end in 5.

(ii) starts with 1–0, and since (iii) is twice the divisor, the divisor is less than 50.

Suppose the divisor is even. Then (ix) (−10) must be the divisor × 5; ∴ it must be less than 50 × 5; ∴ it must be 210 or 110.

If (ix) is 110, then the divisor is 22 and (iii) would be 44, which is absurd; ∴ (ix) is not 110.

If (ix) is 210, then the divisor is 42 and (vii) would end in an even number, but in this case the first figure of (viii) cannot be 2. ∴ the divisor is not 42.

∴ The divisor ends in 5 and the second figure of (iii) is 0. The divisor goes only twice into 1–0; ∴ it cannot start with 1 or 2; ∴ it must be 45 or 35. If it is 45, then (ix) is 45 × 4 or 6 or 8. But 45 × 4 = 180; 45 × 6 = 270; 45 × 8 = 360. And the second figure of (ix) is 1, ∴ the divisor is not 45; ∴ it must be 35; ∴ (iii) is 70, and the first figure of (iv) cannot be more than 3. ∴ it is 3, and (ii) starts with 100. (iv) is 30–; ∴ (v) is 280 (35 × 8).

∴ The first figure in (iv) is 2.

The last figure in (vii) is 0 or 5, but not 0, for (viii) cannot start with 7; ∴ it is 5; ∴ (viii) and (ix) are 210. And (vii) can only be 245 (35 × 7).

*Complete Solution*

```
              2 8 7 0 · 6
    35 ) 1 0 0 4 7 1
         7 0
         ─────
         3 0 4
         2 8 0
         ─────
           2 4 7
           2 4 5
           ─────
             2 1 0
             2 1 0
             ═════
```

# 25. Seven Digits Divided by Two Digits

```
          _ _ _ _ _ . _      (i)
  _ _ ) _ _ _ _ _ _ _         (ii)
      _ _                     (iii)
      ___
        _ _                   (iv)
        _ _                   (v)
        ___
        _ _ _                 (vi)
          _ _                 (vii)
          ___
          _ _ _               (viii)
          _ _ _               (ix)
          ___
            _ _ _             (x)
            _ _ _             (xi)
            ===
```

(ii) must start with 10, and (iii) must start with 9.

Similarly, (vi) must start with 10, and (vii) must start with 9. The divisor must go into 9–.

(v) is a multiple of the divisor, but it cannot start with 9; if it did, there would be no first figure of (vi).

It is not possible for (iii) to be 90, for (iv) would then be at least 10–. ∴ the divisor cannot end in 0, and it cannot be 45.

The last figure in (x) and (xi) is 0, and since the divisor cannot end in 0 or 5 it is an even number, and the last figure in (i) is 5. Divisor cannot end in 5, for (iii) would then be 95, or 5 × 19.

Suppose (iii) is 92. Then the divisor would be 46 (not 23, for the divisor must be even).

(iv) would then start with 8 or 9, and it would not be possible for (vi) to start with 1. ∴ (iii) is not 92.

Suppose (iii) is 94. Then the divisor could only be 47. But the divisor must be even.

Suppose (iii) is 98. Then the divisor could only be 49. But the divisor must be even.

∴ (iii) must be 96 and (vii) must be 96.

∴ (viii) starts with 4 or more, and the divisor must be at least 40 or it would not have been necessary to bring down the third figure in (viii). ∴ the divisor must be 48 (there is no other number between 40 and 50 that goes exactly into 96).

∴ (v) is 48, and since (vi) starts with 10, (iv) is 58 ( ∴ there must be no more 5's). (viii) is 4—; ∴ (ix) must be either 432 (48 × 9) or 384 (48 × 8). But if (ix) was 432, then (viii) would have to be 456—but there are no more 5's.

∴ (ix) must be 384.

*Complete Solution*

Add up from the bottom and we have the following:

```
                  2 1 2 0 8 · 5
        4 8 ) 1 0 1 8 0 0 8
              9 6
              ───
                  5 8
                  4 8
                  ───
                  1 0 0
                    9 6
                    ───
                        4 0 8
                        3 8 4
                        ───
                          2 4 0
                          2 4 0
                          ═══
```

# 26. Six Digits Divided by Two Digits: Figures Given All Wrong

```
                  – – – –          (i)
    2 2 ) – 0 – – – –              (ii)
          8 9                      (iii)
        ─────────
          – – –                    (iv)
        1 1 9                      (v)
        ─────────
          – –                      (vi)
        6 0                        (vii)
        ─────────
          – –                      (viii)
          – –                      (ix)
        ─────────
```

(The reader is advised to make a diagram like the following in which he or she can fill in the correct figures as they are discovered.)

```
                  – – – –          (i)
    – – ) – – – – – –              (ii)
          – –                      (iii)
        ─────────
          – – –                    (iv)
          – – –                    (v)
        ─────────
          – –                      (vi)
          – –                      (vii)
        ─────────
          – –                      (viii)
          – –                      (ix)
        ─────────
```

Since the figures in the quotient are all different and there are 3 two-figure numbers [(iii), (vii), and (ix)], the divisor cannot be more than 33 ($34 \times 3 = 102$). The first figure in (ii) must be 1, and (ii) starts at least with 11–. If (iii) starts with 7 (e.g., 79 or less), then the divisor is at least $\frac{78}{3} = 26$.

But in that case the divisor would go 4 times into 11–, and (iii) would have 3 figures. ∴ (iii) cannot start with 7 or less and as it is not 8– (the figure given), it must be 9–.

The divisor does not start with 2 (figure given); ∴ it starts with 3 or 1. Suppose it starts with 1. Then 19 × 9 = 171. But we know that (v) does not start with 1 (figure given); ∴ the divisor must start with 3. ∴ the divisor must be 30, 31, 32, or 33. But it is not 30, for (vii) would then end in 0, but it does not (figure given). And it is not 33, for (iii) would then end in 9, but it does not (figure given). And it is not 32, for 2 is the second figure of the divisor. ∴ the divisor is 31, and (iii) is 93.

(iv) must start with 6 or 3, but it does not start with 6 (figure given); ∴ it starts with 3, and (vii) is 31; ∴ (ix) must be 62.

(v) must start with 2, and must be 31 × 7 (217) or 31 × 8 (248) or 31 × 9 (279). But it is not 217 or 279; ∴ it is 31 × 8 (248).

*Complete Solution*

Add up from the bottom and we get the following:

$$
\begin{array}{r}
3\ 8\ 1\ 2 \\
31\ )\ \overline{1\ 1\ 8\ 1\ 7\ 2} \\
9\ 3 \\
\hline
2\ 5\ 1 \\
2\ 4\ 8 \\
\hline
3\ 7 \\
3\ 1 \\
\hline
6\ 2 \\
6\ 2 \\
\hline
\end{array}
$$

## 27. Five Digits Divided by Two Digits: Figures Given All Wrong

```
                1 7 8 6        (i)
        3 4 ) 9 - - - -        (ii)
              6 0              (iii)
              ───
              1 - -            (iv)
              2 8 6            (v)
              ─────
                3 - -          (vi)
                1 4 3          (vii)
                ─────
                  3 1 -        (viii)
                  2 - -        (ix)
                  ═════
```

(The reader is advised to make a diagram like the following in which he or she can fill in the correct figures as they are discovered.)

```
              - - - -          (i)
      - - ) - - - - -          (ii)
            - -                (iii)
            ───
            - - -              (iv)
            - - -              (v)
            ─────
              - - -            (vi)
              - - -            (vii)
              ─────
                - - -          (viii)
                - - -          (ix)
                ═════
```

From 1 in (i), the divisor is less than 50; ∴ its first figure must be 4, 2, or 1 (not 3, for this is the figure given). But it is not 1, for 1 in (vii) would then be right (19 × 9 = 171). If it is 4, then since the first figure in (i) would be at least 2, the first figure in (iii) would be at least 8. But this is not possible, for the first figure in (iv) must be at least 2. ∴ the first figure in the divisor can only be 2. ∴ since 29 × 9 is only 261, the first figures of (iv), (v), (vi), (vii), (viii), and (ix) must be 1 or 2. ∴ they can only be 2, 1, 2, 2, 1, 1, in that order.

The first figure in (iii) cannot be 7 or more, for the first figure in (ii) is 8 or less and the first figure in (iv) is 2 or more. ∴ The first figure in (iii) is 5 or less (not 6, the figure given). ∴ The first figure in (i) can only be 2.

The divisor cannot be 20, 21, or 22, for 22 × 9 is only 198 and (vii) starts with 2. If the divisor were 23, then (v) could only be 184 (23 × 8) [remember that (iv) starts with 2]. But 8 is the second figure given in (v). ∴ the divisor is not 23.

The divisor cannot end in 4 (the figure given) or 5, for the second figure of (iii) would then be 0, but it is. ∴ the divisor is 26 or more. ∴ (iii) starts with 5 (26 × 2 = 52). If the divisor were 26, then (v) would be 182 (26 × 7). But 7 is the figure given in (i). ∴ the divisor is not 26.

If it were 27, then (v) would be 189 (27 × 7). But 7 is the figure given. ∴ the divisor is not 27. If it were 28, then (v) would be 196 (28 × 7). But 7 is the figure given. ∴ the divisor is not 28. ∴ the divisor can only be 29. ∴ (iii) is 29 × 2 (58). 29 × 6 = 174; ∴ (v) 174.

(vii) cannot be 203 (29 × 7), for 3 is the figure given in (vii). (vii) cannot be 29 × 8, for 8 is the figure given; ∴ (vii) can only be 29 × 9 (261). (viii) and (ix) must be the same: not 29 × 4 (116), for 1 is the figure given in (viii); not 29 × 6, for 6 is the figure given in (i); not 29 × 7 or more, for 29 × 7 = 203 and this is too much. ∴ (viii) and (ix) can only be 29 × 5, i.e., 145.

*Complete Solution*

Add up from the bottom and we get the following:

```
           2 6 9 5
  2 9 ) 7 8 1 5 5
         5 8
         ─────
         2 0 1
         1 7 4
         ─────
           2 7 5
           2 6 1
           ─────
             1 4 5
             1 4 5
             ═════
```

# 28. The Woogle on the Wardrobe

The possible causes of thud (T) and squeak (S) are woogle (W), chumph (C), pollux (P), Venetian blind (V), and rocking chair (R).

(i) When W, C, and P are fixed, we have V, R $\rightarrow$ S.

(ii) When C, V, and R are fixed, we have W, P $\rightarrow$ neither S nor T.

(iii) When V and W are fixed, we have R, C, P $\rightarrow$ T.

(iv) From (i) and (ii), V, R, W, and P cannot be the cause of T (if they were, T would be present); $\therefore$ C is the cause of T.

(v) From (ii) and (iii), C, P, R, and W cannot be the cause of S; $\therefore$ V is the cause of S.

*Complete Solution*

The chumph causes the thud; the Venetian blind causes the squeak.

# 29. The Quill Quirks

Let us call "Take off little cap on top" A.
Let us call "Press button with 'Beware' " B.
Let us call "Cut open card saying 'Do not touch' " C.
Let us call "Dingle the 'Do not dingle' drum" D.
Let us call "Quill quirking" $q$.
Let us call "Rudder rumbling" $r$.
Let us call "Springs squeaking" $s$.

Then:

(i) A, B $\rightarrow q, r$.

(ii) A, C, D $\rightarrow r, s$.

(iii) B, D $\rightarrow q$.

(iv) From (ii), $q$ is not caused by A, C, or D; $\therefore$ $q$ is caused by B.

(v) From (i) and (iii), $s$ is not caused by A, B, or D; $\therefore$ $s$ is caused by C.

(vi) From (iii), $r$ is not caused by B or D; $\therefore$ $r$ is caused by A or C. But only A is in (i) and (ii); $\therefore$ $r$ is caused by A.

*Complete Solution*

The quill quirking is caused by pressing the button with "Beware"; the springs squeaking is caused by cutting open the card saying "Do not touch"; and the rudder rumbling is caused by taking off the little cap on top.

# 30. Some Private Tattering

(i) No team can play more than 2 matches. If B drew 2, then its goals for should be equal to its goals against. But they are not. ∴ *either* the number of matches that B drew *or* B's goals for or against are wrong. If "C Won" and "C Lost" are correct, then C drew none. But this would mean that the total of draws is odd. But it should be even, as each match appears twice. ∴ the incorrect figure is *either* A's or B's draws *or* "C Won" or "C Lost." Since there is only one incorrect figure, it must be B's draws. This should be 1. ∴ All other figures are correct.

(ii) ∴ B lost 1 and drew 1. And since B and C played 2, A played 2. And we can fill up the table thus:

|   | Played | Won | Lost | Drawn | Goals for | Goals against |
|---|--------|-----|------|-------|-----------|---------------|
| A | 2 | 1 | 0 | 1 |   | 0 |
| B | 2 | 0 | 1 | 1 | 2 | 3 |
| C | 2 | 1 | 1 | 0 |   | 6 |

(iii) A vs. B was drawn. A had no goals against it. ∴ the score of A vs. B was 0–0. ∴ the score of B vs. C was 2–3. C had 6 goals against it, 2 by B and ∴ 4 by A. And since A had no goals against it, the score of A vs. C was 4–0.

*Complete Solution*

| A vs. B | 0–0 |
|---|---|
| A vs. C | 4–0 |
| B vs. C | 2–3 |

# 31. "Such Stuff as Dreams Are Made Of"

(i) If (4) is true, then E became the BW; ∴ (2) is true (if E is the BW, then D is not the BW) and (1) is true (if E is the BW, then E is not the DO). But we are told that only 2 predictions were true. ∴ (4) cannot be true. ∴ E did not become the BW. A diagram will help, thus:

|  | Bottle washer | Welfare officer | Door shutter | Door opener | Worker |
|---|---|---|---|---|---|
| Alf |  |  |  |  |  |
| Bert |  |  |  |  |  |
| Charlie |  |  |  |  |  |
| Douggie |  |  |  |  |  |
| Ernie | X |  |  |  |  |

The fact that E is not the BW has been put in. The reader is advised to put in other information on his or her own diagram.

(ii) Consider (5). If it is true, then (2) is true; ∴ D is not the BW. And all other predictions must be false (for only 2 predictions were true). ∴ (3) must be false; ∴ A would be the WO. But we are told that the WO made one of the true predictions; ∴ our assumption is wrong; ∴ (5) is not true. ∴ B's prediction is not true; ∴ D became the BW.

(iii) ∴ predictions (4), (5), and (2) are false. ∴ predictions (1) and (3) are true. ∴ from (1), E is not the DO, and from (3), A is not the WO.

(iv) A and C (who made correct predictions) are between them the WO and the worker. But we know that A did not become the WO; ∴ C became the WO and A became the worker. ∴ by elimination B became the DO and E became the DS.

Alf became the worker; Bert became the door opener; Charlie became the welfare officer; Douggie became the bottle washer; and Ernie became the door shutter.

# 32. Wage Negotiation on the Island of Imperfection

(i) Suppose B3 is true. Then C is a Pukka, and since B has made a true remark, B is a Sh-Sh and A is a W-W. ∴ C3 is false; ∴ C cannot be a Pukka. ∴ our assumption is wrong; ∴ B3 is false and B1 is false.

(ii) C does not represent a W-W; ∴ C is not a Pukka; ∴ A is a Pukka (no one else can be). ∴ C3 is false and C1 is false.

(iii) From C1 (false), Y is not a Pukka; ∴ Y is a Sh-Sh or a W-W. From A2 (true), X's first remark is false; ∴ X is a Sh-Sh or a W-W. ∴ Z must be a Pukka (neither X nor Y can be). ∴ C2 is true. ∴ C is a Sh-Sh and B is a W-W. From A2, X's first remark is false; ∴ neither B nor C can represent him; ∴ A does. ∴ X is a W-W and Y is a Sh-Sh. So we have the following:

A is a Pukka representing X, a W-W.
B is a W-W representing Z, a Pukka.
C is a Sh-Sh (X, $\sqrt{}$, X) representing Y, a Sh-Sh ($\sqrt{}$, X, $\sqrt{}$).

(iv) From B1 (false), Z's wages are H44 or less. From A3 (true), X's wages are $\frac{1}{2}$ Z's or Y's. But they cannot be $\frac{1}{2}$ of Z's (H44 or less), for wages are between H25 and H85. ∴ X's wages are $\frac{1}{2}$ of Y's. And from A1 (true), Z's wages are H7 less than Y's.

(v) Suppose Z's wages are H44. Then Y's are H51 and X's are not an exact number of H's. Suppose Z's wages are H43. Then Y's are H50 and X's are H25. And if Z's wages are less than H43, X's would be less than H25. But all their wages are between H25 and H85 inclusive. ∴ X's wages are H25, Y's wages are H50, and Z's wages are H43.

### Complete Solution

A is a Pukka and represents X, who is a Wotta-Woppa and whose wages are H25.

B is a Wotta-Woppa and represents Z, who is a Pukka and whose wages are H43.

C is a Shilli-Shalla and represents Y, who is a Shilli-Shalla and whose wages are H50.

# 33. "Who Did It?" on the Island of Imperfection

(i) Suppose C1 and C3 are true (they are both true or both false). Then B stole the watch and A is a Pukka. ∴ A3 is true, and E was telling the truth. But E belongs to the same tribe as B; ∴ C, A, and B all make true statements. But one of them is a W–W. ∴ our assumption is wrong, and C1 and C3 are false.

(ii) ∴ A is not a Pukka, and since C is not, B and E are Pukkas. ∴ B2 is true; ∴ C2 is false; ∴ C and F are W–W's. ∴ A and D are Sh–Sh's.

(iii) We know that the youngest of the 6 is the criminal. From B3 (true), F is 26 (or less) and A is 78 (or less). (Remember that ages are between 20 and 80 inclusive.) If A1 and A3 are true, then B is older than F (A1), and B stole the watch (we know that E is a Pukka). But from B2 (true), "the youngest of the 6 of us is the criminal." ∴ A1 and A3 are false and A2 is true. From A1 (false), B is younger than F. From B1 (true), D is younger than C, and from A2 (true), D is younger than E. ∴ the villain must be either B or D (we know that all the others have someone who is younger than them). But it cannot be B (C1 is false). ∴ it is D.

(iv) We know that F's age is 26 or less, and from A1, B is younger, and since D is the villain, D is younger still. ∴ F is 26, B is 23, and D is 20. And A (3 times as old as F) must be 78. And we know that C and E are between 29 and 75 (inclusive).

D was the villain. The ages of the 6 are as follows:

A  78
B  23
C  between 29 and 75
D  20
E  between 29 and 75
F  26

# 34. A Cold Professor

P stands for "Turn the central heating $\frac{3}{4}$ on."
Q stands for "Turn the central heating $\frac{1}{2}$ on."
R stands for "For increased oil fluidity."
S stands for "Emergency. Press if all else fails."
$x$ stands for "Water dripping from the pipe."
$y$ stands for "The pipes turn blue."
$z$ stands for "A high-pitched scream."

We have the following:

1. P, S are followed by $x$, $z$.
2. Q, R are followed by $x$, $y$.
3. P, R are followed by $y$.

(i) Consider $x$. From (3), neither P nor R could be the cause of $x$, for if they were, $x$ would have followed. ∴ in (1), S must have caused $x$, since we know that P did not. And in (2), Q must have caused $x$, since R did not. ∴ Q and S both cause $x$.

(ii) Consider $y$. From (1), neither P nor S can be a cause of $y$. In (3), R must be a cause of $y$, since P is not. In (2), we know that R is a cause of $y$, but it is possible that Q is too. ∴ R and Q can both cause $y$. ∴ R causes $y$ and Q may do so as well.

(iii) Consider $z$. From (2), neither Q nor R can be a cause of $z$. And from (3), P cannot be. ∴ from (1), S, and only S, can be the cause of $z$.


*Complete Solution*

Turning the central heating $\frac{1}{2}$ on and pressing the "Emergency" button both cause water to drip from the pipe.

Increased oil fluidity causes the pipes to turn blue, and turning the central heating $\frac{1}{2}$ on may do so as well.

Pressing the "Emergency" button causes the high-pitched scream.

# 35. Murder in the Menonly Mansion

(i)  Look first at (6) and try to find out whether B is one of the 4 original brothers (i.e., of the first generation). Suppose B is not. Then B must be of the second generation as, from (1), B has one or more sons.

(ii)  From (2), G is one of the first generation, and from (3), E is G's brother and one of G's and E's other brothers is H's father.

(iii)  If B and his 3 brothers are of the second generation, then *either* D's father (i.e., G's son) *or* H (who is *not* G's son)— or possibly both—are also of the second generation. So we have the following:

First generation—4.

Second generation—B + 3 brothers, and H *or* D's father or both.

And in the third generation we have J (a nephew of B and K), D (G's only grandson), and either in the second or the third generation I, who is an only son and ∴ is *not* B's brother. This makes 12 (at least). But there are only 11. ∴ B must be of the first generation.

(iv)  From (5), K is B's brother, but from (1), K has no sons. ∴ H must be B's son. And we have the following:

| Brian | George | Edgar | Kenneth |
|-------|--------|-------|---------|
| Henry |        |       |         |
|       | Duncan |       |         |

(v)  From (5), J must be G's or E's son, but not G's, for G has a grandson and, from (1), J has no sons, and from (5), no brothers. ∴ J is E's son.

(vi) Consider (4). C cannot be G's son, for I would then be G's grandson, but see (2). And C cannot be K's son (he has none), nor E's (J has no brothers). ∴ C is B's son and I is B's grandson. We know that H has a son [see (1)], and it must be A or F. But it is not A, for H's son can have no sons; ∴ H's son is F, and D's father is A. The only cousin of C's who has a son is A, and his son is D.

*Complete Solution*

The 4 first-generation brothers are Brian, Edgar, George, and Kenneth. Brian has 2 sons, Henry and Colin; Henry has a son, Ferdinand; And Colin has a son, Ivor. Edgar has a son, Julian, but no grandsons. George has one son, Arthur, who has one son, Duncan. Kenneth has no sons.

The murderer is Duncan.

# 36. Nearly Right

(i) Consider A. We have the following:

| Played | Lost | Drawn | Points |
|--------|------|-------|--------|
| 3      | 1    | 2     | 2      |

If one of these figures were changed—e.g., "A Played"—then at least one of the other figures would have to be changed too. And the same thing applies to the matches played, won, lost, and drawn and the points of B, D, and E. ∴ the mistake must be in "C Won" or "C Lost" or in one of the figures for goals for or against. And all other figures are correct.

(ii) "C Played" must be 2 or 4 (to make the total even). And C's points must be 3 or 5 (to make the total even and equal to the total of matches played). C must have drawn 1 (to make the total of drawn matches even), and this drawn match must have been against A. If "C Played" is 2, then since C's points would then be 3, C won 1, drew 1, and lost 0. But we know that C vs. A was drawn and C's other matches must have been against B (who played everyone). But B did not lose a match (7 points); ∴ this is not possible; ∴ C played 4 matches and C's points were 5. ∴ C won 2, lost 1, and drew 1. And "C Won" is the wrong figure.

(iii) The correct table now reads like this:

|   | Played | Won | Lost | Drawn | Goals for | Goals against | Points |
|---|--------|-----|------|-------|-----------|---------------|--------|
| A | 3      | 0   | 1    | 2     |           |               | 2      |
| B | 4      | 3   | 0    | 1     | 5         |               | 7      |
| C | 4      | 2   | 1    | 1     |           | 2             | 5      |
| D | 2      | 0   | 2    | 0     | 3         | 5             | 0      |
| E | 3      | 1   | 2    | 0     | 3         | 2             | 2      |

(iv) A vs. B and A vs. C were drawn. B vs. C, B vs. D, and B vs. E were won. C vs. D and C vs. E were won. D played only 2; ∴ D did not play A or E. ∴ A's third match (lost) was against E. We now know the result of each match.

(v) E won 1 and lost 2 and had 3 goals for it and 2 against it. ∴ the score of E vs. A must have been 3–0, that of E vs. B 0–1, and that of E vs. C 0–1.

(vi) Consider D. D played 2 and lost 2, in each case by 1 goal (D's total of goals was 3–5). But B cannot have gotten more than 3 goals against D, for it only scored 5 goals, and the score of B vs. E was 1–0 and that of B vs. C must have been at least 1–0. ∴ the score of D vs. B was 0–1, 1–2, or 2–3. But it was not 0–1, for the score of D vs. C would then be 3–4, and C only had 2 goals against it. And it was not 1–2, for the score of D vs. C would then be 2–3, and though C had 2 goals against it, at least 1 must have been scored by B. ∴ the score of D vs. B was 2–3; ∴ that of D vs. C was 1–2. Since C had only 2 goals against it, the score of C vs. B was 0–1 and that of C vs. A was 0–0. And since B scored only 5 goals, the score of B vs. A was 0–0.

*Complete Solution*

| | |
|---|---|
| A vs. B | 0–0 |
| A vs. C | 0–0 |
| A vs. E | 0–3 |
| B vs. C | 1–0 |
| B vs. D | 3–2 |
| B vs. E | 1–0 |
| C vs. D | 2–1 |
| C vs. E | 1–0 |

# 37. Tish and the Rajah's Rubies

The Professor gives us a clue by saying that the letters are important. They form a division sum. (It will help to make a diagram with blanks replacing the letters, so that the figures can be filled in as they are found.)

$$
\begin{array}{r}
o-s\ u \quad\quad \text{(i)} \\
n\ u\ )\ -d\ e\ e\ f\ - \quad \text{(ii)} \\
n\ u \quad\quad\quad\quad\quad \text{(iii)} \\
\hline
u\ r\ - \quad\quad\quad \text{(iv)} \\
d\ t\ e \quad\quad\quad \text{(v)} \\
\hline
s\ h\ - \quad\quad \text{(vi)} \\
u\ t\ - \quad\quad \text{(vii)} \\
\hline
d\ f\ d \quad\ \text{(viii)} \\
d\ t\ - \quad\ \text{(ix)} \\
\hline
t \quad\quad \text{(x)} \\
=
\end{array}
$$

(1) The first digit of (ii) must be 1, and the first figure in (i) must be 1. $\therefore o = 1$. The last digit of (ii) must be $d$, and of (iv) must be $e$, and of (vi) must be $f$. And from (vi), (vii), and (viii), the last digit in (vii) must be 0 $(f - 0 = f)$. From (v), *dte* is a multiple of *nu*; $\therefore$ (ix) must be *dte*, and the second digit of (i) is $u$.

(2) From (iv), (v), and (vi), $h = 0$, and (vii) is *uth*. From (vii) $u \times s = -0$; $\therefore$ either $s$ or $u$ must be 5. But not $u$, for if that were so, every multiple of it would end in 0 or 5. But there are 3 different figures in which multiples of $u$ end $(u, e, \text{and } h)$; $\therefore s$ must be 5. $\therefore$ from (vi) and (vii) $u = 4$. From (iv) and (v), $d = 3$.

(3) From (vi), (vii), and (viii), $t = 7$. $\therefore$ the divisor $= \frac{470}{5} = 94$; $\therefore n = 9$. $\therefore$ (v) (*dte*) is $94 \times 4 = 376$. $\therefore e = 6$. $\therefore$ from (ii), (iii), and (iv), $r = 2$. And from (viii) and (ix), $f = 8$.

∴ the division sum is as follows:

```
                                1 4 5 4
              9 4 ) 1 3 6 6 8 3
                      9 4
                      ─────
                        4 2 6
                        3 7 6
                        ─────
                          5 0 8
                          4 7 0
                          ─────
                            3 8 3
                            3 7 6
                            ─────
                                7
                                =
```

Thus:

$h = 0$

$o = 1$

$r = 2$

$d = 3$

$u = 4$

$s = 5$

$e = 6$

$t = 7$

$f = 8$

$n = 9$

And if we replace the numbers in the message by letters, we get the following:

UNDERTHEFOURTEENTHSTONENORTHOFTHE-
NUTTREE

or:

UNDER THE FOURTEENTH STONE NORTH OF
THE NUT TREE

# 38. Not After Jay

For the Professor the cross-number puzzle is clearly of great importance. Let us solve it.

(i) Consider 8 down. From 7 across, the first digit is less than 5; from 9 across, the second digit is even; from 10 across, the last digit is odd. ∴ the two numbers that are multiplied together must both be odd, and must differ by 2. They are not 9 × 11 (99)—too small; nor 11 × 13—both prime; nor 13 × 15 (195)—the second digit is odd; nor 15 × 17 (252)—the second digit is odd; nor 17 × 19—both prime; nor 19 × 21 (299)—the second digit is odd. 21 × 23 (483) is a possibility, and since 23 × 25 is more than 500, it is the only possibility. ∴ 8 down is 483. ∴ the second figure of 9 across is 4. ∴ the second figure of 3 down is 4 (see 3 down). 5 down is a multiple of 3 and of 7, and ∴ of 21. And it ends in 4 (see 5 down and 3 down); ∴ it is 84. ∴ 3 down is 84044.

(ii) Consider 1 down. This must be 840 (any other multiple of 840 has 4 or more figures). ∴ the second figure of 2 down is 1. Since 4 down is even, the last figure is 4 (see 10 across), and 10 across starts with 33.

(iii) Consider 2 down. We know that the second figure is 1. It cannot be 21, for the first figure of 4 down would then be 6—but it must be even. ∴ 2 down is 51, and the first figure of 4 down is 3. 6 across must be 4 1 4 7 4 (the average size of the digits is 4). 7 down must start with 3 ("the same when reversed"). The third digit of 7 across must be 1 or 2, but not 2 (see 4 down); ∴ it is 1. And 4 down must be 3 7 1 3 4, and the first figure of 9 across is 7. ∴ the solution of the cross-number puzzle is as follows:

| | | | | |
|---|---|---|---|---|
| ¹8 | ²5 | ³8 | ⁴3 | ⁵8 |
| ⁶4 | 1 | 4 | 7 | 4 |
| 0 | ⁷3 | 0 | 1 | ⁸4 |
| | ⁹7 | 4 | 3 | 8 |
| ¹⁰3 | 3 | 4 | 4 | 3 |

It is not hard to see that when the Professor talks about Jay he means J (the tenth letter of the alphabet). "Not after Jay" suggests that we should see what happens if we make the numbers 0–9 stand for the letters A–J and read the cross-number puzzle from left to right in the ordinary way. Thus:

0 = A
1 = B
2 = C
3 = D
4 = E
5 = F
6 = G
7 = H
8 = I
9 = J

The message we get is I F I D I E B E H E A D A B E H E D I D D E E D, or IF I DIE BEHEAD ABE. HE DID DEED.

*Complete Solution*

It seems reasonable to conclude, therefore, that Abe was the murderer.

## 39. Addition: Letters for Digits
## (Two Numbers)

| A | B | L | B | (i) |
|---|---|---|---|---|
| B | G | L | B | (ii) |

| L | Z | A | A | (iii) |
|---|---|---|---|---|

In the last line down A must be even (B + B). And since in the third line down L + L produces A, there cannot be anything to carry from the last line down. ∴ B = 0, 1, 2, 3, or 4 and L = 5, 6, 7, 8, or 9. But B cannot be 0; it is not possible to have 0 at the beginning of (ii).

If B were 4, then A would be 8; but 4 + 8 is too large for the first line down. If B were 3, then A would be 6 and L would be 8. But in the first line down 3 + 6 = 9 (not 8).

If B were 1, then A would be 2 and L would be 6. But A + B is not 6.

∴ B must be 2; A = 4; L = 7 [and 4 + 2 + 1 (carried) = 7]. ∴ in the second line down, since there is 1 to carry, G = 8 and Z = 1 (G cannot be 7, for L is 7, and G cannot be 9, for Z would then be 2).

*Complete Solution*

| 4 | 2 | 7 | 2 |
|---|---|---|---|
| 2 | 8 | 7 | 2 |

| 7 | 1 | 4 | 4 |
|---|---|---|---|

# 40. Addition: Letters for Digits (Three Numbers)

$$
\begin{array}{llll}
\text{D} & \text{H} & \text{E} & \text{S} & \text{(i)} \\
\text{J} & \text{H} & \text{H} & \text{S} & \text{(ii)} \\
\text{R} & \text{H} & \text{D} & \text{S} & \text{(iii)} \\
\hline
\text{H} & \text{H} & \text{J} & \text{H} & \text{(iv)} \\
\hline
\end{array}
$$

(1) Consider the first line down. H must be at least 6 (1 + 2 + 3). But if H were 6 in the second line down, we would have [6 + 6 + 6 + (perhaps) 2 to carry], and this could not produce H in (iv) [the second figure in (iv) would then be 8, 9, or 0]. And if H were 7, we would have $7 \times 3 = 21 +$ (perhaps) 2 = 23. And if H were 8, we would have $8 \times 3 = 24 +$ (perhaps) 2 = 26. ∴ we could not have H as the second figure in (iv).

(2) But if H were 9, we would have $9 \times 3 = 27 +$ (perhaps) 2 = 29. ∴ H must be 9 and there is a 2 to carry from the third line down to the second line down.

(3) In the last line down S must be 3, and there is nothing to carry. There is a 2 to carry from the second line down to the first line down; ∴ D, J, and R must be 1, 2, and 4, but we do not yet know which is which. There is a 2 to carry from the third line down to the second line down; ∴ E must be 8 (it cannot be 9), D must be 4 (it cannot be more), and J must be 1 (it cannot be less). ∴ R = 2.

*Complete Solution*

$$
\begin{array}{llll}
4 & 9 & 8 & 3 \\
1 & 9 & 9 & 3 \\
2 & 9 & 4 & 3 \\
\hline
9 & 9 & 1 & 9 \\
\hline
\end{array}
$$

# 41. "I Do Not Wish to Be, I'd Like to Add"

| C | O | M | P | U | T | E | R |
|---|---|---|---|---|---|---|---|
| T | A | P | R | U | R | C | R |

| C | O | A | X | O | X | P | R | O |
|---|---|---|---|---|---|---|---|---|

(i) (ii) (iii) (iv) (v) (vi) (vii) (viii) (ix)

From (i), C must be 1. (The most that can be carried when 2 digits are added together.)

∴ in (ii), C = 1.

We know that O in (ii) is not 1, and it cannot be 2 [1 + 9 + 1 (carried) = 11]; ∴ O = 0.

∴ there cannot be anything to carry from (iii), O + A = A [and there cannot be anything to carry from (iv)]. ∴ T = 9 (1 + 9 = 10).

In (ix), R is not 0; ∴ R = 5 [and there is a 1 to carry from (ix) to (viii)]. ∴ in (viii), E = 3. ∴ in (vii), P = 4.

In (vi), X must be odd (U + U + 1); ∴ X must be 7 (the only odd number left). And since there is a 1 to carry from (vi) to (v), U = 8. ∴ in (iv), M = 2, and in (iii) A = 6 (the only digit left).

*Complete Solution*

```
  1 0 2 4 8 9 3 5
  9 6 4 5 8 5 1 5
  ─────────────────
1 0 6 7 0 7 4 5 0
```

## 42. Addition: Letters for Digits
## (Four Numbers: One Letter Wrong)

```
X  T  M  B
W  H  M  W
T  T  M  W
M  X  M  B
----------
B  B  B  B
==========
(i) (ii) (iii) (iv)
```

We must first look for the incorrect letter.

(1) Consider (i). Since X, W, T, and M are different, they must be at least $1 + 2 + 3 + 4$, i.e., 10. But this is not possible, for B cannot be more than 9. ∴ the mistake must be in X, W, T, or M in (i) [not in B, for whatever B is, (i) would still be wrong]. From (iv), B must be even $(B + W + W + B)$. And from (i), it must be at least 7 $(1 + 1 + 2 + 3)$, when we have found the letter in (i) that is incorrect. ∴ B must be 8.

(2) In (iv), W must be 1 or 6 $(8 + 1 + 1 + 8 = 18; 8 + 6 + 6 + 8 = 28)$. But in (iii), since B is even and $4 \times M$ is even, there must be a 2 to carry from (iv). ∴ W = 6. ∴ in (iv), M = 4.

(3) Consider (i) again. If W were 6, and one of the others is wrong, (i) is not possible $(6 + 1 + 1 + 2 = 10)$. ∴ W cannot be 6, and this must be the mistake. ∴ M is 4 in (i). ∴ X in (i) must be 1 or 2 and T in (i) must be 2 or 1, and (i) is [1 (or 2) + 1 + 2 (or 1) + 4], i.e., 8, and there is nothing to carry from (ii). ∴ (ii) is [2 (or 1) + H + 2 (or 1) + 1 (or 2) + 1 (carried)], and this comes to 8.

(4) If H were 0, then this could not be more than $(2 + 0 + 2 + 1 + 1)$, i.e., 6, which is not enough. H cannot be 1 or 2, for X and T are 1 and 2 or 2 and 1, and it cannot be 4, for $M = 4$. And if H were 5, then (ii) would be at least $(1 + 5 + 1 + 2 + 1)$, i.e, 10 (too much). $\therefore$ H can only be 3. $\therefore$ T = 1 and X = 2. And W in (i) should be T (1).

*Complete Solution*

W in (i) should be T (1).

$$
\begin{array}{cccc}
2 & 1 & 4 & 8 \\
1 & 3 & 4 & 6 \\
1 & 1 & 4 & 6 \\
4 & 2 & 4 & 8 \\
\hline
8 & 8 & 8 & 8 \\
\hline
\end{array}
$$

# 43. Cross-Number Puzzle (3 by 3)

5 across must be less than 32, for 32 × 32 = 1024, and from 1 across, the square of 5 across has 3 figures. But 1 down is even; ∴ 5 across can only start with 2. Since 2 down is odd, 5 across must be 21, 23, 25, 27, or 29.

The first digit of 1 down can only be 6 or 8. ∴ 5 across must be at least 25 ($25^2 = 625$). But the last digit of 1 across would then be 5, and 3 down could only be 55 (but "the digits are different"). If 5 across were 27, then 1 across would be 729; but the digits of 1 down are all even. ∴ 5 across must be 29, and 1 across is 841. ∴ 2 down is 459, 3 down must be 19, and 4 across must be 459.

*Complete Solution*

# 44. Cross-Number Puzzle (3 by 3)

(i) 1 across (2 digits) is $\frac{1}{2}$ of 2 down (3 digits). ∴ 2 down must start with 1 (99 × 2 = 198). ∴ 1 across must be 61, 71, 81, or 91 (it must be more than $\frac{1}{2}$ of 100, and it is not 51, for 2 down would then be 102, and there are no 0's).

(ii) The last figure in 2 down must be 2 (2 × 1). Since the first digit of 1 across is 6, 7, 8, or 9, the second digit of 2 down must be 2, 4, 6, or 8. But it is not 2 or 4 (see 3 across); ∴ the first digit of 1 across must be 8 or 9.

(iii) Consider 3 across. It must be 246 or 468. Suppose 1 across is 81. Then 3 across would be 246. But this is not possible, for the third digit of 1 down would be 0 (and there are no 0's). ∴ 1 across must be 91. And 3 across is 468. ∴ 1 down is 963.

(iv) The sum of the digits of 4 across is at least 13. ∴ the first figure must be at least 8. But since 3 down is odd, it must be 9.

*Complete Solution*

# 45. Cross-Number Puzzle (5 by 5)

(i) Consider 6 down and 7 across. The digits of 7 across are all even; the only 3-figure perfect cubes that have an even number as their second digit are 125, 343, and 729. But 7 across must be either 2468 or 8642, so the second figure cannot be 2. ∴ it is 4, and 6 down is 343 and 7 across is 2468.

(ii) ∴ the first 2 digits of 5 across are 12. 1 down must be 21 or 91, but not 21 (see 1 across); ∴ it is 91, and 1 across is 93.

(iii) Consider 2 down. The last 2 digits must add up to 17; ∴ they must be 9 and 8, in that order (see 8 across). 8 down is even; ∴ 9 across must be 28 (see 1 across).

(iv) Consider 3 down. At the moment this is − − 6 − −. The fourth figure must be 1, 5, or 7 (see 8 across), and the second figure must be greater than 3 (see 5 across). But the square of 5− or 7− has 4 figures; ∴ the fourth figure is 1. And 3 down must be 25616 (*not* 19614 because of 5 across).

(v) The last digit of 8 across must be 5 or 7. But it is not 5 (see 5 across and 4 down); ∴ it is 7; ∴ the second digit of 4 down is 7. And the first digit of 8 across is 5.

(vi) The second digit of 3 across is the same as the second digit of 10 across. 3 across must be 23 or 29, but 10 across can only be 69 (63 is not the multiple of 2 primes).

*Complete Solution*

| 1 9 | 2 3 | ■ | 3 2 | 4 9 |
|---|---|---|---|---|
| 5 1 | 2 | 6 3 | 5 | 7 |
| ■ | 7 2 | 4 | 6 | 8 |
| 8 5 | 9 | 3 | 1 | 7 |
| 9 2 | 8 | ■ | 10 6 | 9 |

# 46. Cross-Number Puzzle (5 by 5)

(i) 6 across cannot end in 1 or 9 (see 2 down). And it cannot end in 5, for 6 down would then have to end in either 0 (but there are no 0's) or 5 (but the digits of 9 across are all even). ∴ 6 across must by 16, 36, or 64. If it were 64, 6 down would be 640 (the only multiple of 64 starting with 6), but there are no 0's.

∴ 6 across is 16 or 36; ∴ the third figure of 2 down is 6 and the fourth figure must be 7 or 8. If 6 across is 36, then 6 down would have to be 324, 360, or 396. But none of these is possible (there are no 0's, and see 8 across). ∴ 6 across is 16 and 6 down is 176 (as the second figure of 6 down must be 7 or 8). ∴ the second figure of 9 across must be 8.

(ii) 3 across is a multiple of 176, and it must start with a number less than 6, but not 1 (see 2 down), and it cannot be 176 × 2 (352) (see 4 down); ∴ it must be 528. ∴ the last figure of 4 down is 2 and the last figure of 9 across is 4.

(iii) The first figure of 7 across is also the third figure of 4 down and the first figure of 8 across (i.e., these are the 3 times when it appears). The only figures that have not yet appeared are 3 and 9. But the last digit of 1 down cannot be 3; ∴ it must be 9, as are the second and third figures of 4 down. ∴ 5 down can only be 84.

(iv) 1 across is 84 × an even number, and we know that the first figure of 1 across is 6 or less and that the last figure of 1 across is 4 or less. The only possibility is 672. ∴ 1 down is 6789.

|   |   |   |   |   |
|---|---|---|---|---|
| ¹6 | 7 | ²2 | ■ | ■ |
| 7 | ■ | ³5 | ⁴2 | ⁵8 |
| 8 | ⁶1 | 6 | ⁷9 | 4 |
| ⁸9 | 7 | 7 | 9 | ■ |
| ■ | ⁹6 | 8 | 2 | 4 |

# 47. Cross-Number Puzzle (5 by 5)

(i) 6 across must be 19, 38, 57, 76, or 95. But the third digit of 2 down cannot be 9 or 8, and the first digit of 6 down cannot be 9 (no 3-figure perfect cube starts with 9); ∴ 6 across is 57 or 76; ∴ 6 down must be 512 or 729. 8 across is a perfect square doubled and then reversed; ∴ it must start with an even number; ∴ 6 down must be 729; ∴ 6 across is 76.

(ii) 8 across is 2 – –; it is an even number, and the sum of the digits is 18. The second figure must be 7 or 8 (see 2 down); ∴ the third figure must be 9 or 8. But it is not 9 (it must be even); ∴ 8 across is 288. ∴ the last figure of 2 down is 9.

(iii) 9 down (8–) is a multiple of 19, 29, 39, or 49, and it is odd. It can only be 29 × 3 = 87. ∴ the first figure of 2 down is 2 and the fourth figure of 1 across is 2.

(iv) 7 down is the first 3 digits of 2 down rearranged. 2 and 6 are two of the digits, and the other digits must be odd (see 11 across) and, from 2 down, must be 3 or 5. ∴ 3 down is a factor of 73 or 75. 73 has no factors, and if 3 down were 73, 1 across would be –272– and it would not be possible for the digits of 1 across to add up to 24 *and* for the first digit to be the same as the last. ∴ the last digit of 11 across and the second digit of 2 down must be 5. ∴ 3 down is a factor of 75 and must be 25 (the middle figure of 1 across must be even—see above). And the first and last figures of 1 across must be 9.

(v) 4 down is a multiple of the square of 55, i.e., of 3025; ∴ 4 down must be 9075.

(vi) 7 down is either 265 or 625. If it is 265, the sum of the digits of 7 across is 9, and of 10 across is 11; if it is 625, the sum of the digits of 7 across is 13, and of 10 across is 7. ∴ 7 down is 265 (see 7 across).

*Complete Solution*

| | | | | |
|---|---|---|---|---|
| ¹9 | ²2 | ³2 | 2 | ⁴9 |
| ■ | ⁵5 | 5 | ■ | 0 |
| ⁶7 | 6 | ■ | ⁷2 | 7 |
| ⁸2 | 8 | ⁹8 | ¹⁰6 | 5 |
| ¹¹9 | 9 | 7 | 5 | ■ |

# 48. Cross-Number Puzzle
# (5 by 5, with One Clue Incorrect)

We must first try to find out more about the clue that is incorrect.

(i) 7 across must be 21, 42, 63, or 84. In no case is the first digit odd. ∴ *either* 3 down *or* 7 across is the incorrect clue. ∴ all other clues are correct.

(ii) Consider 12 across and 11 down. Since 11 down is even, 12 across is the square followed by the cube of an even number. The first 2 digits of 12 across must be the square and the last 3 digits the cube. The only possibilities are 36216 and 64512. But the sum of the digits of 11 down is 12; ∴ it is not possible for the first digit to be 2 (the second would then be 10). ∴ 12 across is 36216 and 11 down is 66.

(iii) Consider 10 across and 4 down. Since the first digit of 10 across is even, it can only be 66. ∴ 4 down is 98761 and 5 down is 89. Since 7 across ends in 7 (to make 4 down correct), 7 across must be the incorrect clue [see (i) above].

(iv) 9 down is a multiple of 7 ending in 6; ∴ it must be 56. And 8 across is 75. ∴ 5 down is 89.

(v) Consider 1 across and 1 down. From 1 down, the first digit must be 1, 5, or 9. But it is not 1 (too small) and not 9; ∴ it is 5. ∴ the first digit of 6 across is 1 or 9. If it is 1, then 6 across starts with 178; if it is 9, 6 across starts with 979. In both cases the second digit is 7. ∴ the first digit of 2 down is 6, and 1 across is 56798.

(vi) The third digit of 6 across is 8 or 9, but it is not 9 (see 3 down); ∴ 8. And 3 down is 781. And 1 down is 51973. ∴ 7 across is 17.

*Complete Solution*

7 across is the incorrect clue.

The correct figures are as follows:

| 1 5 | 2 6 | 3 7 | 4 9 | 5 8 |
|-----|-----|-----|-----|-----|
| 6 1 | 7 | 8 | 8 | 9 |
| 9 | ■ | 7 1 | 7 | ■ |
| 8 7 | 9 5 | ■ | 10 6 | 11 6 |
| 12 3 | 6 | 2 | 1 | 6 |

# 49.  Cross-Number Puzzle
# (5 by 5, with One Clue Incorrect)

We must first try to find the incorrect clue.

(i)  7 across could be 125, 216, 343, 512, or 729, so the second figure could be 1, 2, or 4. 6 down could be 19, 38, 57, 76, or 95, so the second figure could be 5, 6, 7, 8, or 9. ∴ it is not possible for the second figure of 7 across to be the same as the second figure of 6 down; but they must be the same. ∴ *either* 7 across *or* 6 down must be the incorrect clue. ∴ all the other clues are correct.

(ii)  Consider 1 across. The last figure must be 7 or 9. ∴ 4 down starts with 7 or 9; ∴ it must be the square of 31 (961) (the squares that start with 7 are those of 27 and 28, neither of which is a prime).

(iii)  5 across can only be 23456. The first digit of 8 across must be less than 5 (see 3 down), but it cannot be 1. ∴ 8 across is 31. And the last 2 digits of 3 down are 2 and 1. ∴ the first digit of 9 across is 2. ∴ 5 down is 282; ∴ 7 across is the incorrect clue (no 3-figure perfect cube starts with 8). ∴ 6 down is correct, and is therefore 38.

(iv)  The fourth digit of 2 down is at least 6, and it is the same as the first digit of 10 down (see 9 across). ∴ 10 down must be 65 or 91, but not 91 (see 2 down); ∴ it is 65; ∴ 9 across is 2662.

(v)  The first 2 digits of 11 across must be 57, 58, or 59 (see 2 down). But they are not 58, for they must add up to an even number. And they are not 57, for the last 2 digits would then add up to 6 and would be 1 and 5. ∴ they are 59, and 11 across is 5916.

(vi)  Consider 2 down. The third digit must be 5. And the first digit must be 1 or 3, but not 1 (see 1 across); ∴ it is 3. And 1 across must be 1379.

*Complete Solution*

7 across is the incorrect clue.

The correct figures are as follows:

|   | 1 | 3 | 7 | 9 |
|---|---|---|---|---|
| 2 | 3 | 4 | 5 | 6 |
| 8 | 8 | 5 | 3 | 1 |
| 2 | 6 | 6 | 2 |   |
|   | 5 | 9 | 1 | 6 |

# 50. Five Digits Divided by Two Digits

$$\begin{array}{r} a\ t\ p \\ y\ h\ )\ \overline{h\ m\ m\ x\ m} \\ h\ x\ d \\ \hline k\ x\ m \\ h\ p\ x \\ \hline k\ x \end{array}$$

    (i)
(ii)
(iii)

(iv)
(v)

(vi)

(The reader is advised to make a diagram like the following and to fill in the digits as they are discovered.)

$$\begin{array}{r} -\ -\ - \\ -\ -\ )\ \overline{-\ -\ -\ -\ -} \\ -\ -\ - \\ \hline -\ -\ - \\ -\ -\ - \\ \hline -\ - \end{array}$$

Since 2 figures are brought down in (iv), $t$ in (i) is 0. From (ii) and (iii), $m - x = 1$. $\therefore m = x + 1$. And from (iv), (v), and (vi), $m = x + x$. $\therefore x + 1 = x + x$, and $x = 1$. $\therefore m = 2$.

Since (v) ends in 1, the divisor is odd; $\therefore h$ is odd. But it is not 1, for $x = 1$. And it is not 9, for if $h$ in (v) were 9, then $k$ would have to be 10. And it is not 5, for if the divisor ends in 5, $x$ in (v) could not be 1. $\therefore h$ must be 3 or 7.

Suppose $h$ were 7. Then $p$ in (i) would be 3 [$7 \times 3 = 21$, and (v) ends in 1]. Then (v) cannot be more than $97 \times 3$, which is less than 300. But we are assuming that $h$ [the first figure of (v)] is 7. $\therefore h$ cannot be 7 and must be 3. $\therefore p$ is 7. And $k$ in (iv) is 4. $\therefore d$ in (iii) is 8.

The divisor is $\frac{371}{7}$, i.e., 53. $\therefore y = 5$, and $a$ in (i) is 6.

179

*Complete Solution*

```
              6 0 7
5 3 ) 3 2 2 1 2
      3 1 8
      ─────
          4 1 2
          3 7 1
          ─────
            4 1
            ═══
```

# 51. Five Digits Divided by Two Digits

$$
\begin{array}{r}
a\ l\ x\ j \qquad\text{(i)} \\
l\ x\ \overline{)\ j\ b\ q\ x\ j} \qquad\text{(ii)} \\
s\ j \qquad\qquad\text{(iii)} \\
\hline
x\ q \qquad\qquad\text{(iv)} \\
d\ l \qquad\qquad\text{(v)} \\
\hline
h\ s\ x \qquad\quad\text{(vi)} \\
h\ d\ x \qquad\quad\text{(vii)} \\
\hline
l\ y\ j \qquad\text{(viii)} \\
l\ y\ j \qquad\text{(ix)}
\end{array}
$$

(It will help to have a diagram with blanks replacing the letters, so that the figures can be filled in as they are found.)

(1) From (vi), (vii), and (viii), $x - x = y$. $\therefore y = 0$.

(2) When the divisor ($lx$) is multiplied by $x$, the result [see (vii)] is $hdx$. $\therefore x$ must be 5 or 6. If $x$ is 5, then whatever $lx$ is multiplied by, the result can end only in 5 or 0. But the result of multiplying $lx$ by $a$, $l$, $x$, and $j$ produces 3 different numbers ($j$, $l$, and $x$). $\therefore x$ is not 5. $\therefore x = 6$.

(3) (v) is $lx$ multiplied by at least 2. If $l$ was 3, then $d$ would be 6. But it cannot be, for $x = 6$ and $d$ cannot be greater than 6. $\therefore l$ is not 3. $\therefore l$ is 1 or 2.

(4) If $l$ were 1, then the divisor would be 16, and (vii) ($lx$ times $x$) would be 96. But (vii) has 3 figures. $\therefore l$ is *not* 1; $\therefore l = 2$.

(5) $\therefore$ (v) is $26 \times 2 = 52$. $\therefore d = 5$; $\therefore$ from (iv), (v), and (vi), $h = 1$.

(6) (iii) must be the only other 2-figure multiple of 26, i.e., 78. $\therefore s = 7$ and $j = 8$.

(7) From (ii), (iii), and (iv), $b = 4$. And since $78 = 26 \times 3$, $a = 3$. From (iv), (v), and (vi), $q = 9$.

181

*Complete Solution*

```
                    3 2 6 8
        2 6 ) 8 4 9 6 8
               7 8
               ___
               6 9
               5 2
               ___
               1 7 6
               1 5 6
               ___
                 2 0 8
                 2 0 8
                 ===
```

182

# 52. Six Digits Divided by Three Digits

$$
\begin{array}{r}
a\ e\ m\ d \qquad \text{(i)} \\
p\ e\ c\ \overline{)\,l\ e\ d\ g\ a\ h} \qquad \text{(ii)} \\
c\ l\ d \qquad\quad \text{(iii)} \\[4pt]
\hline
p\ c\ b\ g \qquad\quad \text{(iv)} \\
p\ a\ p\ p \qquad\quad \text{(v)} \\[4pt]
\hline
h\ e\ a \qquad\qquad \text{(vi)} \\
g\ d\ m \qquad\qquad \text{(vii)} \\[4pt]
\hline
p\ b\ e\ h \qquad \text{(viii)} \\
p\ b\ c\ g \qquad \text{(ix)} \\[4pt]
\hline
l\ p \qquad\qquad\ \text{(x)}
\end{array}
$$

(It will help to have a diagram with blanks replacing the letters, so that the figures can be filled in as they are found.)

(1) From (ii), (iii), and (iv), $d - d = b$. $\therefore b = 0$.

(2) The following letters are used; $a$, $b$, $c$, $d$, $e$, $g$, $h$, $l$, $m$, and $p$, making 10. $\therefore$ each figure appears. Let us try to find out which letter is 1. We know that $b = 0$, and $a$, $e$, $m$, and $d$ are not 1, for no figure in (i) can be 1. From (ii) and (iii), $l$ is greater than $c$; $\therefore l$ is not 1. From (iv) and (v), $c$ is greater than $a$; $\therefore c$ is not 1. From (vi) and (viii), $h$ is greater than $g$; $\therefore h$ is not 1. (vii) ($gdm$) is the divisor ($pec$) multiplied by 2 or more. $\therefore g$ is greater than $p$; $\therefore g$ is not 1. $\therefore p$ must be 1 (no other figure can be).

(3) We know that the last digit of (iv) is greater than 1; $\therefore$ by considering the third digits of (iv) and (v) we see that the first digit of (vi) must be 9. $\therefore h = 9$.

(4) $\therefore$ from (viii), (ix), and (x), $g = 8$. And from (iv), (v), and (vi), $e = 7$.

(5) 17– multiplied by 7 produces 1–11; $\therefore$ it must be 173; $\therefore c = 3$. $\therefore$ from (iv) and (v), $a = 2$. And from (viii), (ix), and (x), $l = 4$. And from (vi), (vii), and (viii), $m = 5$. And from (vi), (vii), and (viii), $d = 6$.

*Complete Solution*

```
                    2 7 5 6
        1 7 3 ) 4 7 6 8 2 9
                3 4 6
                ─────
                1 3 0 8
                1 2 1 1
                ─────
                  9 7 2
                  8 6 5
                  ─────
                  1 0 7 9
                  1 0 3 8
                  ─────
                      4 1
                      ═══
```

# 53. Uncle Bungle Relapses

$$
\begin{array}{r}
\phantom{m d )}\; u\;\; d\;\; h\;\; t \qquad \text{(i)} \\
m\, d\, ) \;\overline{t\;\; t\;\; u\;\; r\;\; r} \qquad \text{(ii)} \\
r\;\; p \phantom{\;\; u\;\; r\;\; r} \qquad \text{(iii)} \\
\hline
g\;\; d\;\; u \phantom{\;\; r} \qquad \text{(iv)} \\
g\;\; u\;\; t \phantom{\;\; r} \qquad \text{(v)} \\
\hline
d\;\; r\;\; r \qquad \text{(vi)} \\
d\;\; r\;\; t \qquad \text{(vii)} \\
\hline
g \phantom{\;\; r} \qquad \text{(viii)} \\
\hline
\end{array}
$$

(The reader is advised to make a diagram like the following and to fill in the digits as they are discovered.)

$$
\begin{array}{r}
- \; - \; - \; - \\
- \, - \, )\; \overline{- \; - \; - \; - \; -} \\
- \; - \phantom{\; - \; - \; -} \\
\hline
- \; - \; - \phantom{\; -} \\
- \; - \; - \phantom{\; -} \\
\hline
- \; - \; - \\
- \; - \; - \\
\hline
- \\
\hline
\end{array}
$$

We must first try to find out more about the letter that is wrong.

(1) In (ii), (iii), and (iv) we have $\dfrac{r}{g}\;^{t}$. $\therefore$ if all is correct, $t$ must be greater than $r$.

(2) In (vi), (vii), and (viii) we have $\dfrac{drt}{g}\;^{drr}$. $\therefore$ if all is correct,

$r$ must be greater than $t$. ∴ *either* the $t$ in (ii) *or* the $r$ in (iii) *or* the $r$ in (vi) *or* the $t$ in (vii) must be wrong. ∴ everything else is correct.

(3) Since 2 figures are brought down in (vi), $h = 0$. Since (iii) has 2 figures and is not the divisor, $m$ is less than 5. $g$ and $d$ [in (v) and (vii)] must both be less than $m$, for if they were not, the third figure in (v) and (vii) would not be needed. And from (iv) and (v), $d - u = 1$. ∴ $m$ is greater than $g$, $d$, $u$, and $h$. ∴ $m$ must be at least 4. And since $m$ is less than 5, $m = 4$. From (iv) and (v), $d$ is greater than $u$. And from (i), $u$ cannot be 1 [for (iii) is not the divisor]. ∴ $d = 3$, $u = 2$, and $g = 1$.

(4) From (iv), (v), and (vi), $t = 9$. And from (ii), (iii), and (iv), $p = 6$. (iii) is the divisor (43) times 2, i.e., 86. ∴ $r = 8$. ∴ the mistake must be in (vi) or (vii). (vii) is $43 \times 9$, i.e., 387. ∴ $t$ in (vii) should be 7, *not* 9.


*Complete Solution*

The mistake is $t$ in (vii); it should be 7, not 9. (There is no letter for 7.)

The division sum is as follows:

$$
\begin{array}{r}
2\ 3\ 0\ 9 \\
4\ 3\ \overline{)\ 9\ 9\ 2\ 8\ 8} \\
8\ 6\phantom{\ 2\ 8\ 8} \\
\hline
1\ 3\ 2\phantom{\ 8\ 8} \\
1\ 2\ 9\phantom{\ 8\ 8} \\
\hline
3\ 8\ 8 \\
3\ 8\ 7 \\
\hline
1
\end{array}
$$

# 54. An Error Again

$$
\begin{array}{r}
g \ k \ q \ h \qquad \text{(i)} \\
h \ g \ \overline{)\ c \ g \ m \ p \ i \ c} \qquad \text{(ii)} \\
e \ q \ d \qquad\qquad\quad \text{(iii)} \\
\hline
g \ g \ p \qquad\qquad \text{(iv)} \\
e \ h \ m \qquad\qquad \text{(v)} \\
\hline
h \ p \ i \qquad\quad \text{(vi)} \\
d \ d \ d \qquad\quad \text{(vii)} \\
\hline
k \ e \ c \qquad \text{(viii)} \\
k \ p \ i \qquad \text{(ix)} \\
\hline
k \qquad\quad \text{(x)} \\
=
\end{array}
$$

(It will help to have a diagram with blanks replacing the letters, so that the figures can be filled in as they are found.)

We must first try to find out more about the incorrect letter.

(1) From (ii) and (iii), $c - e = 1$; from (iv) and (v), $g - e = 1$. But this is not possible. $\therefore$ the first figure of (ii) ($c$) or the first figure of (iii) ($e$) or the first figure of (iv) ($g$) or the first figure of (v) ($e$) must be wrong. $\therefore$ all other figures are correct.

(2) From (iv), (v), and (vi), $m = 0$. $\therefore$ $hg$ goes exactly into $--0$; $\therefore$ $g$ must be 2, 4, 5, 6, or 8. But if $g$ were 5, (iii), (vii), and (ix) would all end in 5 (we know they do not end in 0). But this is not possible, for there are 2 letters here ($d$ and $i$); $\therefore$ $g$ is not 5. If $g$ were 6, then $h6 \times 6$ would produce in (iii) a number ending in 6. But it does not [(iii) ends in $d$]. $\therefore$ $g$ is not 6. $\therefore$ $g$ is 2, 4, or 8.

(3) Since the third figure of (ii) is 0, from (iii) and (iv), $d + g = 10$. $\therefore$ $d = 8$, 6, or 2. If $g = 2$, then $d = 8$. $\therefore$ $hg \times g$ ($h2 \times 2$) should end in 4 in (iii), but it ends in $d$ (8). $\therefore$ $g$ is not 2. If $g = 8$, then $d = 2$; $\therefore$ $hg \times g$ ($h8 \times 8$) should end in 4 ($8 \times 8 = 64$) in (iii), but it ends in $d$ (2).

∴ $g$ is not 8; ∴ $g = 4$ and $d = 6$. [We must remember that the first figures of (ii), (iii), (iv), and (v) are suspect and should not be filled in until we have discovered which is incorrect.]

(4) We know that (vii) (666) is a multiple of the divisor ($h4$), and that the divisor goes $q$ times into it. $666 = 2 \times 3 \times 3 \times 37$. We know that $q$ is not 6, for $d = 6$. ∴ $q = 9$. ∴ the divisor $= \frac{666}{9} = 74$; ∴ $h = 7$.

(5) $74 \times k$ ends in 0 [(v)]; ∴ $k = 5$. And (ix) $= 74 \times 7 = 518$. ∴ $p = 1$ and $i = 8$. From (vi), (vii), and (viii), $e = 2$. And from (viii), (ix), and (x), $c = 3$.

(6) ∴ (iii) $= 74 \times 4 = 296$; $q = 9$, and the first figure in (ii) is 3. And (v) $= 74 \times 5 = 370$; ∴ the first figure in (v) should be $c$, *not* e, and this is the mistake. [The first figure in (iv) is 4 ($g$), and this of course is correct.]

*Complete Solution*

The incorrect letter is the first letter of (v) ($e$). It should be $c$. The division sum is as follows:

```
              4 5 9 7
    7 4 ) 3 4 0 1 8 3
          2 9 6
          ───────
            4 4 1
            3 7 0
            ───────
              7 1 8
              6 6 6
              ───────
                5 2 3
                5 1 8
                ───────
                    5
                  ═══
```

# 55. Douggie Was Dumb

(i) Consider C's remark. If it is false, then C is a Pukka; but he has then made a false remark, which is not possible. C's remark cannot be false. ∴ it is true, and C is not a Pukka. But since it is true, C cannot be a W-W. ∴ C is a Sh-Sh.

(ii) ∴ E's remark must be true (there is one representative of each tribe). ∴ E must be a Pukka (E cannot be a W-W). ∴ D is a W-W.

*Complete Solution*

Charlie is a Shilli-Shalla.
Douggie is a Wotta-Woppa.
Ernie is a Pukka.

# 56. The Un-Flats

(i) If B1 is true, than A1 is true and C2 is true. But this is not possible, as one of them is a W-W, whose statements are all false. ∴ B1 is false.

(ii) A1 and C2 cannot both be false, since one of the three is a Pukka, whose statements are all true. ∴ C2 must be true, and A1 may be true or false.

(iii) If C1 is true, then C is a Pukka (2 true remarks). But if C1 is true, C is a Sh-Sh (numbers 11–20 are reserved for Sh-Shs). ∴ C1 is false. ∴ C is a Sh-Sh, but does not live in number 18.

(iv) Neither B nor C is a Pukka (each has made a false statement). ∴ A is a Pukka, and both A's statements are true. ∴ B is a W-W, and B2 is false.

(v) Since A2 is true, B lives at number 7.

(vi) And since A1 is true, A must live at number 24 or number 28. But we know that A's number is not a multiple of 12 (B1 is false); ∴ A lives at number 28.

(vii) From B2 (false), C's number is a multiple of 6. But it is not 18 (C1 is false). ∴ C's number is 12.

*Complete Solution*

Askew is a Pukka and lives at flat number 28.
Bent is a Wotta-Woppa and lives at flat number 7.
Crooked is a Shilli-Shalla and lives at flat number 12.

# 57. Ages and Wages

(i) B3 and B4 cannot both be true. For C would then be a Pukka, and since B has made 2 consecutive true statements, he would have to be a Pukka too. ∴ B is not a Pukka.

(ii) Suppose B3 is true and B4 is false. Then C would be a Pukka, B a Sh-Sh, and A a W-W. But this is not possible, for B4 would then be true. Suppose B3 is false and B4 is true. Then A is a W-W, B is a Sh-Sh, and C would have to be a Pukka. But C is not a Pukka, for B3 is false. ∴ B3 and B4 are both false, and B is a W-W. And since B3 is false, A must be a Pukka and C a Sh-Sh.

(iii) B1 is false; ∴ A's age is 35 or more. A1 is true; ∴ A's wages are greater than A's age; ∴ A's wages are H36 or more. Since A's wages are between H36 and H41, they cannot be $m(7)$; ∴ C2 is false; ∴ C1 and C3 are true. (C is a Sh-Sh.) Since A3 is true, A's wages must be H36; ∴ A's age must be 35.

(iv) Consider C1 and A2 (both true). C's age cannot be 35 (the same as A's), nor 40, nor 30 (it is not possible for B's wages to be halfway between A's and C's). ∴ C's age must be 25 and B's wages must be H30.

(v) From B2 (false), B's age is less than or equal to C's. But it cannot be equal, for all ages are different. ∴ it must be less than C's. ∴ B's age must be 24; and from C3, C's wages are H24.

*Complete Solution*

A is a Pukka, his age is 35, and his wages are 36 hopes.
B is a Wotta-Woppa, his age is 24, and his wages are 30 hopes.
C is a Shilli-Shalla, his age is 25, and his wages are 24 hopes.

# 58. Crooked Crescent

(i) If B1 is true, then C1 is false; ∴ A2 is false; ∴ B would be the Pukka. ∴ B2 is true. ∴ A1 could not be true, for A's number would then be 8, and A would have to be a W-W. ∴ A1 would be false. ∴ C would be a Sh-Sh; ∴ C2 is true (C1 is false). But if A is a W-W, A's number cannot be 7. ∴ our original assumption must be false. ∴ B1 is false.

(ii) ∴ C1 must be true; ∴ A2 is true. ∴ A and C both make true statements; ∴ B is a W-W, and both remarks are false. ∴ B's number is not a prime; ∴ it must be 4, 6, 8, 9, or 10.

(iii) If A1 is true, then A's number must be 7 (in no other way can A's number be a prime, 3 greater than 4, 6, 8, 9, or 10, and not greater than 10). ∴ if A1 is true, then C2 is true. But A and C would then *both* be Pukkas, which is not possible. ∴ A1 is false; ∴ A is a Sh-Sh. ∴ C is a Pukka, and C2 is true.

(iv) Since C2 is true, A's number is 7. From A2 (true), B's and C's numbers differ by 1, and from A1 (false), we know that B's number is not 4. ∴ since B's number must be 6, 8, 9, or 10 and C's must be 1, 2, 3, or 5, the only possibility is for B's to be 6 and for C's to be 5.


*Complete Solution*

A is a Shilli-Shalla and lives at number 7.
B is a Wotta-Woppa and lives at number 6.
C is a Pukka and lives at number 5.

# 59. Ladies on the Island

(i) Suppose B1 is true. Then B is not a W-W, and B3 is true. ∴ C is a W-W; ∴ C1 is false; ∴ A is a W-W. But C and A cannot *both* be W-W's. ∴ B1 cannot be true and must be false. ∴ B is a W-W.

(ii) Consider A1. If it is false, then *neither* A *nor* C is a Pukka. But one of them must be. ∴ A1 is true. ∴ C is a Pukka and A must be a Sh-Sh (with the first and third statements true and the second statement false).

(iii) From B2 (false), B's number is 4. From A3 (true), the Sh-Sh's number (A's) is a multiple of 9. From C2 (true), C's house (i.e., the Pukka's house) is not 13. ∴ from C3 (true), A's number is *not* 9 (9 + 4 = 13). ∴ A's number (from A3) is 18 or 27. But it is not 27, for 27 + 4 = 31, and there are only 30 houses on the street. ∴ A's number is 18; ∴ C's number is 22.

*Complete Solution*

A is a Shilli-Shalla and lives at number 18.
B is a Wotta-Woppa and lives at number 4.
C is a Pukka and lives at number 22.

# 60. Pay Claims

(i) Suppose B1 is true. Then A is a Pukka. ∴ A3 is true. ∴ C is a Sh-Sh. ∴ B, A, and C have all made true remarks. But this is not possible (one of them is a W-W). ∴ B1 is not true.

(ii) ∴ B makes a false remark. ∴ B is not a Pukka. And since B1 is false, A is not a Pukka. ∴ C must be a Pukka. ∴ A3 is false.

(iii) Since A3 is false, A1 is false, and since B1 is false, B3 is false. C1 is true; ∴ C's wages are not a multiple of H5. From A1 (false), we know that B's wages are greater than A's; from C2 (true), we know that A's wages are greater than C's. ∴ C's wages are at least H20.50. ∴ A's wages cannot be *both* H6 less than B's *and* H9 greater than C's (making H15 between higher and lower wages, whereas it can only be H14.50). ∴ B2 must be false. ∴ by elimination, A2 must be true.

(iv) C's weekly wages must be at least H20.50. ∴ from C2, A's wages must be at least H29.50. These two add up to H50. From A2, the weekly wage bill for all of them is H80. ∴ B's wages must be H30 [not less, for B's wages are greater than A's; and not more, to make the total H80 (A3 is true)].

*Complete Solution*

A is a Shilli-Shalla.
B is a Wotta-Woppa.
C is a Pukka.
A's wages are H29.50.
B's wages are H30.00.
C's wages are H20.50.

# 61. Clubs for the Boys

(i) Suppose B1 is true. Then C must be a Pukka and B a Sh-Sh (B has made at least one true statement—B1). ∴ C3 could not be true. But this is contrary to our supposition, which must therefore be wrong. ∴ B1 is false; ∴ B3 is false.

(ii) From B1 (false), C makes fewer true statements than B, or the same number as B. ∴ C is a Sh-Sh or a W-W. ∴ A3 is false; ∴ A1 is false.

(iii) From B3 (false), A belongs to HY. ∴ C1 is false; ∴ C3 is false. ∴ C is a W-W, and C2 is false.

(iv) We know that A1 is false [see (ii)]; ∴ B does not belong to HA. And since A belongs to HY, B2 is false; ∴ B is a W-W.

(v) C2 is false; ∴ C does belong to UO. ∴ by elimination, B belongs to RQ. ∴ A2 is false; ∴ A is a W-W.


*Complete Solution*

A, B, and C are all Wotta-Woppas.
A belongs to the Help Yourselves Club.
B belongs to the Richer Quicker Club.
C belongs to the Up and Over Club.

# 62. Tribal Merging

(i) If S2 is true, S1 must be false; if S2 is false, S1 must again be false (otherwise S is a Sh-Sh). ∴ S1 is false. Since S1 is false, what M said yesterday about T (S1) is not evidence.

(ii) Consider T2. If this is true, then S is more truthful than T. But we know that S makes 1 false statement [see (i)]; ∴ T would have to make 2 false statements. ∴ T2 cannot be true. ∴ S's number is smaller than T's; ∴ T1 is true and S2 is false. ∴ M is a Pukka, with both statements true.

(iii) Since M1 is true, T's number is 40 or 32. But it is not 40, for T would then have to be most truthful. ∴ T's number is 32. ∴ S's number (less than T's) must be 30 or 31. If S's number is 31, then from M2 (true), M's number is 37. But from T1 (true), M's number is *not* a prime. ∴ S's number must be 30 and M's number must be 36.

*Complete Solution*

Mingle is a Pukka and lives in wigwam number 36.
Single is a Wotta-Woppa and lives in wigwam number 30.
Tingle is a Shilli-Shalla and lives in wigwam number 32.

# 63. Emblems Are Out

(i)  Suppose B1 is false. Then A is a W-W; ∴ all A's statements are false. ∴ A3 is false; ∴ C's third remark is not true. ∴ C1 is not true (C1 and C3 are true or false together); ∴ A is a Sh-Sh.

But this is contrary to our original assumption that A was a W-W. ∴ our assumption must be false; ∴ B1 must be true.

(ii)  ∴ B3 must also be true. ∴ A must have 2 or 3 true remarks (A and B are equally truthful). ∴ A1 and A3 must both be true.

(iii)  Since A3 is true, C's third remark is true; ∴ C's first remark is also true. ∴ A is not a W-W nor a Sh-Sh (C1). ∴ A is a Pukka.

(iv)  From B3 (true), B must have 3 true remarks. ∴ C2 is true; ∴ C4 is true. ∴ we now know that all remarks are true.

(v)  Consider B2 and C3. From C3, C's number *reversed* must be 64, 32, or 16. And from B2, C's number is 2 × a prime. But C's number cannot be 61 (too large), nor 23 (a prime number, not twice a prime number); ∴ C's number must be 46.

(vi)  From A2, A's number, larger than C's (see A1 and C4) and a multiple of 8, must be 48. And B's number (between A and C) must be 47.


*Complete Solution*

A, B, and C are all Pukkas.
A's number is 48.
B's number is 47.
C's number is 46.

# 64. Imperfect Telephone Numbers

(i) Suppose B2 is true. Then C is a Pukka; ∴ C2 is true; ∴ A is a W-W. ∴ A1 is false; ∴ B does *not* belong to a more truthful tribe than A does; ∴ A's tribe is *as* truthful or *more* truthful than B's. But according to our assumption, B makes a true statement and A makes none. ∴ our assumption is wrong; ∴ B2 is false; ∴ B4 is false and C is not a Pukka.

(ii) Consider A1. If this were true, then A would be a Sh-Sh with his first remark true (not a W-W, for we are assuming that A1 is true), and B would be a Pukka. But we know that B is not a Pukka (B2 is false). ∴ A1 is false; ∴ A3 is false.

(iii) ∴ B1 is true; ∴ B3 is true. And since A1 is false, A's tribe is *as* truthful or *more* truthful than B's; ∴ A is a Sh-Sh, and A2 is true and C2 is false.

(iv) Since A3 is false, the Sh-Shs' numbers are not 10 to 39. We know that B's number is $m(13)$ and that A's number is 24 less (B3), and that A and B are both Sh-Sh's. If B's number was 91, then A's would be $91 - 24 = 67$, but this is not possible, for A and B belong to the same tribe. Similarly, B's number cannot be 78 but it can be 65 ($65 - 24 = 41$), and this is the only possibility. ∴ B's number is 65 and A's number is 41.

(v) Suppose C3 is false. Then the Pukkas' numbers must be 10 to 39 and the W-Ws' numbers must be 70 to 99. But from B4 (false), C's number is less than A's (i.e., less than 41). And this is not possible if C is a W-W. ∴ C3 must be true; ∴ C must be a Sh-Sh. ∴ C's number must be 40 (there is no other possibility).

*Complete Solution*

A, B, and C are all Shilli-Shallas.
A's telephone number is 41.
B's telephone number is 65;
C's telephone number is 40.

# 65. The Older, the Truer

(i) Consider A2. If this was false, then B was *not* lying when he said that C was a Sh-Sh. ∴ C is a Sh-Sh. And since A has made a false remark, he is not a Pukka; ∴ B is a Pukka, A is a W-W, and C is a Sh-Sh. ∴ B2 should be true (B is a Pukka). But if A is older than B, he is more truthful; ∴ B cannot be a Pukka. ∴ if A2 is false we have a contradiction. ∴ A2 must be true. ∴ B *was* lying when he said that C was a Sh-Sh; ∴ C is not a Sh-Sh.

(ii) Suppose B2 is false. Then B is older than A; ∴ B must make 2 true remarks (we know that A makes 1); ∴ B2 cannot be false. ∴ B2 is true.

(iii) ∴ C must be a W-W (no one else is). And since B2 is true, A is a Pukka and B is a Sh-Sh.

(iv) ∴ the order of ages is A, B, C. From C2 (false), the difference between A's and B's ages is 8 or more. And from C1 (false), A's age is not 40. And from A1 (true), B's age must be halfway between A's and C's. The possibilities are, therefore, the following (if the difference between ages is 8):

| A | 39 | 38 | 37 | 36 |
|---|----|----|----|----|
| B | 31 | 30 | 29 | 28 |
| C | 23 | 22 | 21 | 20 |

And if the difference is 9 the possibilities are as follows:

| A | 39 | 38 |
|---|----|----|
| B | 30 | 29 |
| C | 21 | 20 |

(It is not possible for the difference to be more than 9.)

(v) From B1 (false), we know that A's age is a prime number; ∴ A's age is 37 (the only prime number for A among the possibilities just listed).

*Complete Solution*

A is a Pukka.
B is a Shilli-Shalla.
C is a Wotta-Woppa.
A's age is 37.
B's age is 29.
C's age is 21.

# 66. Top Teams Only

(i) Consider A: It played 1 and drew 1, but its goals were 2–3. This is not possible. ∴ A is not the Pukka team.

(ii) Consider C: It won 1, but made only 1 point. ∴ C is not the Pukka team.

(iii) ∴ B is the Pukka team. And we have the following:

|   | Played | Won | Lost | Drawn | Goals for | Goals against | Points |
|---|---|---|---|---|---|---|---|
| A |  |  |  |  |  |  |  |
| B | 2 | 1 | 0 | 1 | 3 | 1 | 3 |
| C |  |  |  |  |  |  |  |

Consider the drawn matches. Suppose "A Drawn" (1) is correct (so that A is the Sh-Sh team). Then C must be the W-W team and "C Drawn" must be 1. But this is not possible, for the total of drawn matches must be even. ∴ "A Drawn" is wrong, and must be 0 or 2. But it is not 2, for if "A Drawn" is wrong, then "A Won" is wrong and must be 1, and this would make 3 matches played. ∴ "A Drawn" is 0, and "C Drawn" must be 1.

(iv) ∴ "C Won" is also wrong (whether C is W-W or Sh-Sh). It cannot be 2 (this would make 3 matches played); ∴ it is 0. And since "A Drawn" is wrong, "A Won" is wrong, and must be 1. ∴ 2 matches are won (by A and B) and 1 drawn. ∴ 3 matches are played; ∴ "C Played" (2) is correct, and C is the Sh-Sh team; ∴ A is the W-W team.

(v) We now have the following:

|   | Played | Won | Lost | Drawn | Goals for | Goals against | Points |
|---|---|---|---|---|---|---|---|
| A | 2 | 1 | 1 | 0 | 1 or 3 | 2 or 4 | 2 |
| B | 2 | 1 | 0 | 1 | 3 | 1 | 3 |
| C | 2 | 0 | 1 | 1 | 3 | 4 or 2 | 1 |

C lost 1 and drew 1; ∴ C's goals against must be 4 and not 2.

(vi) The score of B vs. C (drawn) must be 0–0 or 1–1 (B has only 1 goal against it). ∴ the score of B vs. A must be 3–1 or 2–0 (see B's totals of goals). Since the score of C vs. B is 0–0 or 1–1, that of C vs. A is 3–4 or 2–3 (see C's totals of goals). ∴ the score of A vs. B is 1–3 or 0–2 and that of A vs. C is 4–3 or 3–2.

(vii) A diagram will help here:

|   | A | B | C |
|---|---|---|---|
| A |   | 1–3<br>0–2 | 4–3<br>3–2 |
| B | 3–1<br>2–0 |   | 0–0<br>1–1 |
| C | 3–4<br>2–3 | 0–0<br>1–1 |   |

We know that A's goals must be 1 or 3 for and 2 or 4 against. ∴ it is not possible for A's scores to be 1–3, 4–3. ∴ they must be 0–2 (vs. B) and 3–2 (vs. C). ∴ the score of B vs. C must be 1–1 (to make B's total 3–1).

*Complete Solution*

A vs. B    0–2
A vs. C    3–2
B vs. C    1–1
A is a Wotta-Woppa.
B is a Pukka.
C is a Shilli-Shalla.

# 67. A Shilli-Shalla at Heart

(i)   It will be useful to set out the remarks as follows:

To A: 1. My wife's name is Jennifer.
       2. B2 is false.
       3. C3 is true.

To B: 1. The number of my house is less than 50.
       2. My wife's name is Dora.
       3. The number of my house is odd.

To C: 1. The sum of the digits of the number of my house is even.
       2. The number of my house is a multiple of 8.
       3. My remarks to A are those of a Sh-Sh.

(ii) Suppose A3 is true; ∴ C3 is true; ∴ A's remarks are those of a Sh-Sh. ∴ A1 is true and A2 false; ∴ from A1, UB's wife's name is Jennifer, and from A2 (false), B2 is true; ∴ his wife's name is Dora. But we know that his wife's name is *either* Jennifer *or* Dora—not both. ∴ our assumption is false. ∴ A3 is false; C3 is false.

(iii) ∴ UB's failure is in his remarks to A; ∴ his remarks to B and C are those of a Sh-Sh. ∴ C1 is false and C2 is true.

(iv) Since C2 is true, the number of UB's house is a multiple of 8; ∴ it is even: ∴ B3 is false. ∴ B1 is false and B2 is true.

(v) ∴ UB's wife's name is Dora; ∴ A1 is false. And since B2 is true, A2 is false. ∴ A2 is the remark that failed UB on his test.

(vi) Consider B1 (false), B3 (false), and C2 (true). From these, we know that the number of UB's house is *not* less than 50, that it is even, and that it is a multiple of 8. ∴ it must be, 56, 64, 72, 80, or 88 (houses are numbered from 1 to 95). And from C1 (false), we know that the sum of the digits of the number is odd. ∴ the number must be 56 or 72.

*Complete Solution*

A2 was the remark on which Uncle Bungle failed.
His wife's name is Dora.
The number of his house is 56 or 72.

# 68. New Arrivals on the Island

(i) Suppose Y2 is true. Then both Z's statements are true. And since Y has made a true statement, X must be a W-W (with no true statements) and Y a Sh-Sh. And since both Z's statements are true, "X's number is a multiple of 8" (Z1); ∴ X's number must be a multiple of 4; ∴ X1 is true. But on our assumption X is a W-W with 2 false statements; ∴ our assumption leads to a contradiction and must be wrong. ∴ Y2 is false.

(ii) ∴ Y is not a Pukka and Z is not a Pukka; ∴ X is a Pukka with 2 true statements; ∴ X's number must be 4 or 8 (X's statements are true; the Pukka's number is between 1 and 10).

(iii) Since X2 is true, Y must be a Sh-Sh (whose number is between 11 and 20). And Z must be a W-W, with a number between 21 and 30. ∴ Y1 is true, and Z1 and Z2 are false.

(iv) From Z1 (false), X's number is not a multiple of 8. ∴ X's number is 4. From Y1 (true), Z's number is even; ∴ from X2 (true), Y's number (11 less than Z's) must be odd. From Z2 (false), Y's number is not a prime. ∴ Y's number must be 15 (the only odd number between 11 and 20 that is not a prime). ∴ from X2 (true), Z's number is 26.

*Complete Solution*

X is a Pukka, with the number 4.
Y is a Shilli-Shalla, with the number 15.
Z is a Wotta-Woppa, with the number 26.

# 69. Ugly, Stupid, and Toothless

(i) Consider A3. If this is true, then A must be a W-W or a Sh-Sh (see details of wages and tribes). But he is not a W-W, for we are assuming that A3 is true; ∴ A would be a Sh-Sh and B would be a Pukka. ∴ B3 would be true, but this is not possible. ∴ our assumption is false; ∴ A3 is not true.

(ii) ∴ A1 is not true. ∴ B is not a W-W. If B is a Pukka, then B3 would be true, but this is not possible. ∴B is a Sh-Sh.

(iii) Consider A2. If it is true, then A's wages = $\frac{75}{100} \times \frac{120}{100}$ (of B's or C's wages). ∴ A's wages = $\frac{3}{4} \times \frac{6}{5} = \frac{18}{20}$ (of B's or C's wages). ∴ A's wages are a multiple of 18, i.e., H18 or H36. But they can only be H18, if A is a Pukka, but A is not; and they can only be H36 if A is a W-W, and if A2 is true, then A is not a W-W. ∴ A2 is not true, and A is a W-W.

(iv) ∴ B2 is false (we know that B is a Sh-Sh). ∴ B1 and B3 are true. Since B3 is true, C is a Pukka, and C1, C2, and C3 are true.

(v) From C2 (true), 2 of the wages are in the ratio of 85:100, i.e., 17:20. No one gets wages of more than 39; ∴ the wages of one must be H17 and of another H20. And it must be B (Sh-Sh) who gets H20 and C (Pukka) who gets H17.

(vi) From C3, S is a Sh-Sh; ∴ S is B. From C1, U must be A and T must be C.

(vii) A's wages are between H30 and H39. But they are *not* H30 (A3 is false), and *not* H37 (B1 is true).


*Complete Solution*

A is a Wotta-Woppa; his wages are between H31 and H39 inclusive, but excluding H37; and his name is Ugly.

B is a Shilli-Shalla; his wages are H20; and his name is Stupid.

C is a Pukka; his wages are H17; and his name is Toothless.

# 70. Uncle Bungle Looks at the Family Tree

(i) Suppose E is a Pukka. Then from E3, C is a Pukka; ∴ from C2, F is a W-W. ∴ F2 is false; ∴ E1 is false. But this is contrary to our hypothesis; ∴ E cannot be a Pukka.

(ii) Suppose E is a W-W. ∴ E1 is false; ∴ F2 is false, and from E3, C is not a Pukka. And D cannot be a Pukka, for D1 would then be false. ∴ our assumption is false and E is not a W-W. ∴ E must be a Sh-Sh of some sort. And either C or F is a Pukka (not both—see C2).

(iii) We know that F3 is true; ∴ C2 is false. ∴ F is a Pukka (no one else can be). ∴ F2 is true. ∴ E1 is true and E3 is false.

(iv) F1 is true; ∴ E is F's son. If E's other parent was a W-W, E would be an ordinary Sh-Sh. But we know that E's remarks are "true, ?, false." ∴ E's other parent must be a Sh-Sh. ∴2 of E's remarks must be true. ∴ E2 is true. ∴ D is E's father. ∴ F must be E's mother.

(v) C1 is false (we know that D is male). ∴ D2 cannot be true, for C makes 2 false statements. And D is not a W-W, for D3 is true. ∴ C must be a W-W, and C3 is false. ∴ C is D's father, and D1 is true.

*Complete Solution*

Clarence is a Wotta-Woppa.
Dimble is either an ordinary Shilli-Shalla or a Pukka-Shilli-Shalla.
Evelyn is a Pukka-Shilli-Shalla.
Fresco is a Pukka.
Clarence is the father of Dimble (male), who is married to Fresco. Evelyn is the son of Dimble and Fresco.